Sussex Wild Flowers

Mary Briggs MBE

Foreword by Professor David Bellamy

Production by Henri Brocklebank and Richard Cobden

ISBN 1-898388-17-2

Sussex Wildlife Trust, Woods Mill, Henfield,
West Sussex BN5 9SD
01273 492630
www.sussexwt.org.uk

First edition published by Sussex Wildlife Trust 2004

Printed and bound by Gemini Press Ltd, Shoreham-by-Sea

Cover Simon Colmer

Back Cover Arthur Hoare (top), Michael Hollings (middle), Alan Knapp (lower)

Frontispiece Pat Donovan

The photographs in this book originate as follows:

Kathleen Amoore: p36
Mary Briggs: p27, 63, 198
Tony Buckwell: p125
Ernie Burt: p50
John Cole: p135
Pat Donovan: p97
Neil Fletcher: p121, 137, 166,
Betty Goddard: p205
Paul Harmes: p128, 129, 130
Arthur Hoare: p10, 21, 25, 31, 34, 64, 77, 78, 85,
89, 90, 91, 96, 99, 103, 112, 113, 119, 120, 122, 123,
124, 131, 132, 138, 140, 143, 147, 151, 173, 180,
191, 201, 215
Michael Hollings: p3, 39, 48, 154, 155, 156, 175
Arthur Hollman: p205
Alan Knapp: p11, 12, 16, 17, 18, 19, 22, 24, 27, 33,
37, 38, 46, 53, 58, 59, 62, 66, 69, 76, 79, 81, 83, 87,
88, 94, 98, 100, 101, 105, 114, 127, 135, 136, 139,
158, 162, 164, 165, 172, 182, 183, 187, 189

David Lang: p14, 15, 20, 35, 49, 51, 55, 56, 57, 60,
65, 71, 72, 82, 84, 93, 106, 107, 116, 121, 145, 152,
153, 160, 161, 167, 190, 192, 196
Arnold Madgewick: p185
Harry Montgomery: p8, 26, 54, 43, 70, 82, 110,
157, 170, 171
John Patmore: p111
Ron Payne: p118
David Plummer: pv, vi, 7, 13, 67, 194
www.davidplummerimages.co.uk
Nick Sturt: p22, 41, 44, 47, 54, 61, 73, 74, 75, 86,
95, 109, 115, 133, 128, 129, 130, 136, 144, 148, 149,
150, 163, 168, 169, 179, 181, 184, 188, 192, 193
Sussex Wildlife Trust: p9, 21, 27, 68, 80, 153,
159, 185, 197

Copyright of all photographs remains with the photographers.
Copyright of frontispiece remains with the artist.

No part of this publication may be transmitted in any form or by any means, electronic or
mechanical, including photocopy, recording, or any information storage and retrieval system
without permission in writing from the publisher.

Contents

spring flowers – March to May

early summer flowers – May to July

late summer flowers – July to September

autumn – September to October

Appendices

Acknowledgments

Writing the descriptions and researching the information on so many plants was a considerable task and the author wishes to acknowledge with thanks the many who have helped in this project. Most importantly thanks goes to the members of the Sussex Botanical Recording Society, without whom we would not have such an understanding of the flora of our counties.

Sussex Wild Flowers started as an idea many years ago and the kind support of Gemini Press has made it possible, particularly the support of Nigel Holmes. All the photographs in this book are the work of local botanists. They have all allowed us access to their wonderful array of images free of charge and we are very lucky to have so many talented botanical photographers in Sussex. All the photographs used are acknowledged at the front of the book. Special thanks go to Arthur Hoare for his contribution to the difficult task of selecting the images to be used. The artwork of the beautiful frontispiece is the work of local botanical artist Pat Donovan, who painted the picture especially for this book to illustrate the joy of painting wild flowers.

On a practical level I must thank Jan and Roger Briggs who typed all the original manuscript from my handwritten notes. Ryan Kelly, John Hallissey and Julian Scobie at Gemini Press must be thanked for their patience and support along with a large array of readers. These include Frances Abraham, Peter Anderton, Alan Gillham, Alan Knapp, Bob Platt, Amanda Solomon and Nick Sturt. Thanks also to Richard Cobden from the Sussex Wildlife Trust who is responsible for all the layout and design and Henri Brocklebank of the Sussex Biodiversity Record Centre who has co-ordinated the production of the book.

Mary Briggs MBE

Foreword

by Professor David Bellamy

Sussex by the Sea

It was in the immediate post war years that I got on my bike and cycled down to the sea through a countryside bursting with biodiversity. Sussex was a county of small farms wreathed in well laid hedgerows and estates of various sizes managed by game keepers of the Richard Jefferies Ilk.

I didn't know the names of all the wild flowers but the Downs were redolent with their palette of colours and the rather sickly scent of Bird's-foot Trefoil. These were all heralded by the song of the Sky Lark above. It was in the cool, dank woods of the Wealden clays that I first learned about dinosaurs and saw Herb-Paris. In still, acid waters I marvelled at Bladderwort, one of the few plants that has turned the tables on the animal world. Of course, in Sussex I enjoyed the mass of bluebells, recently voted Britain's favourite wild flower.

As this superb little book shows, these flowers are still there waiting to be discovered by any natural historian willing to take a walk on the wild side of sunny Sussex.

Bedburn 2004

v

Downland flowers

For my family, Jenny and David,
Roger and Jan, Philip, Becky and Georgina.

In 1722 James Petiver and William Sherard, apothecary botanists,
visited Joseph Andrews at his Apothecary in Sudbury, Suffolk and
described him as *"a curious and obliging botanist"*. He took them to
see some local wild flowers of special interest.

I would like to thank the many *"curious and obliging botanists"*
who have helped me with studies of wild plants in Sussex and
beyond – over many years.

Introduction

Sussex Wild Flowers refers to wild flowers found across the counties of East and West Sussex including Brighton and Hove. Sussex is particularly diverse, from the open, chalk grasslands of the South Downs, to the claggy, clay woodlands of the Weald; from the urban areas to the heaths and the shingle beaches and sand stretching along our coastline. This wide variety of natural and man-made habitats leads to an equally wide range of wild flowers and this book goes part way in capturing that magnificent variety.

Sussex Wild Flowers is written with the desire to inspire an interest in wild flowers and encourage people to get out into the Sussex countryside and see the species and habitats for themselves. Where possible the book advises on where to go in Sussex to see these beautiful plants (often to some rather surprising locations!). It is not, however, intended as a general wild flower identification guide, although it is hoped that the text and pictures will help you to recognise the plants that are described in the book.

Sussex Wild Flowers has been written specifically for non-botanist readers, so the use of technical botanical terms has been avoided as far as possible. Occasionally the use of such a word or phrase is needed, so to help the reader, a glossary is provided on page 212.

Many of the wild plants chosen for this book are now considered rare, but they can all, apart from one (which is sadly now extinct), be found in Sussex today. Of the many species of wild flowers growing in Sussex it was difficult to narrow the list down to those included in this book, but each was chosen for a specific reason. Some are of special interest because they have historical associations with the area, others have been used in medicine or as food or as part of day-to-day life in times past. Many of the species chosen, though a common sight less than 50 years ago, are now rare in Sussex. This is often due to the dramatic difference in land-use over that period.

There can be a great deal of pleasure in being able to identify different flowers and botanical accuracy is not necessary to simply enjoy our local wild flowers. However, for recording purposes, a plant's precise accurate identification is essential, and for this purpose a 'Flora' with keys to names, as well as descriptions and measurements is needed. There are many floras available to suit all botanical standards – several are recommended on page 206. Often a small x10 or x20 magnifying lens is very useful. For a botanist a hand-lens is an invaluable tool that enables the human eye to view the intricate details of a plant's structure. These may include the patterns on an orchid's petal or the hairs down the stem of a Speedwell. These very subtle features may be the only defining characteristic between one species and another. If you require a hand lens to take a closer look at the wild flowers that you see, the details of a hand-lens supplier are given on page 210.

If you want to enjoy wild flowers, photography is a useful tool. All of the pictures included here are the work of local amateur photographers, who often go to extraordinary lengths to capture the image in a specific way. This includes wading into ditches to capture water plants from a water level view-point! In taking photographs of Night-flowering Catchfly with its petals unfurled for this book, and to avoid a midnight expedition, an attempt was made to 'trick' the flower into thinking it was night, by putting a yellow tin over it. It was hoped that by making it dark the flower would act as if it was night time and unfurl its beautiful flowers at a more sociable hour! Alas, it was to no avail, and it was discovered that the only way to capture this Catchfly in its full glory was to go out late at night.

Painting and drawing is another way to enjoy wild flowers. As in photography there is no need to pick the flower to capture it on paper. Simply sitting in a wood or field and drawing and painting in-situ is easily done and is indeed how the beautiful frontispiece for this book was painted.

Knowledge of the distribution of wild flowers in Sussex changes quickly. Between writing this book and going to press new records for some of our rare plants have been found. One of these is the exciting find of an extensive display of Sheep's-bit *Jasione montana* (page 100) on shingle in the far east of Sussex. Sadly some plants may also have been lost. The localities for each species given as of this book were correct in spring 2003.

Some plants are not easily named with accuracy (and may not be growing typically). The Sussex Botanical Recording Society will be happy to help with identification, and are always pleased to have reports of your sightings. If you have an unusual find to report it is helpful if we are contacted without delay – often more difficult plants need confirmation, or a second opinion, so for us to hear of it while the plant is still growing is very helpful.

Thinking of the future, we must do all that we can to safeguard the habitats in which our wild flowers are growing, and it is particularly important to avoid trampling the site. Remember that there may be small seedlings near the flowers, and these can be very inconspicuous and vulnerable.

Though many of the featured flowers may seem unfamiliar to you, all of the species covered would have been familiar to country people, gardeners and apothecaries in Sussex for many hundreds of years, and it is hoped that this book will enable you to look at wild flowers and our Sussex countryside with a new appreciation. We hope that *Sussex Wild Flowers* takes you out and about in our beautiful and varied county, and increases your enjoyment of our wild flowers and the wild places of Sussex.

The Sussex Botanical Recording Society

West Sussex:

Mrs Mary Briggs	9, Arun Prospect, Pulborough RH20 1AL
Dr Alan Knapp	aknapp2000@btinternet.com

East Sussex:

Mr Paul Harmes	10, Hillcroft, Mile Oak Road, Portslade BN4 2QD
	p.harmes01@ntlworld.com
Mr Arthur Hoare	159, St. Mary's Drive, Pound Hill, Crawley RH10 3BG
	arthur@159stm.freeserve.co.uk

Or for help and advice contact:

Sussex Biodiversity Record Centre

Woods Mill, Henfield BN5 9SD
01273 497 553/554
sxbrc@sussexwt.org.uk
www.sxbrc.org.uk

All the author's time, the images, printing and expertise used in creating this book have been provided free of charge. In light of this all the proceeds of this publication will be going to the Sussex Wildlife Trust to support their continued work in taking care of the habitats and species of Sussex.

How to use *Sussex Wild Flowers*

Name in Latin and English including common name, alternative local names and family name.

Details about the plant to help you spot it. Including where it might be found and when it is in flower.

Other plants with a similar appearance.

Plants are grouped by their flowering season (for example late summer) as this is when they are most easily identified.

Main text describing what the plant looks like, where it is found and what it may have been used for or known for in the past; its distribution in Sussex, Britain and the world. Botanical terms are explained in the glossary (see page 212).

Marsh Mallow
Althea officinalis

Mallow family
Malvaceae

Habitat: Coastal and marshy
Height: 1-1.5m
Flowering: August and September
Status: Locally abundant
'Look-alike' plants: Common mallow and tree mallow

This beautiful plant is found growing in slightly saline, marshy sites near the sea, and here it often grows in profusion. It is tall, from 1-1.5m and softly hairy. The velvet-textured leaves are slightly lobed, and are sometimes folded like a fan. The plant has attractive pale pink flowers each about 4cm in diameter, and growing in short-stalked clusters of up to three flowers.

Sixty years ago, marsh mallow was considered to be a rather common plant in marshes near the sea in Sussex, but it is now less common and is more recently only recorded from 20 sites in Sussex. Most records are near the sea and it is often found growing just behind the beach or by the sea wall. It also grows along rivers and it has been found as far inland as Arundel, on the banks of the River Arun, but has only been rarely seen on the River Adur. In East Sussex it grows in the Cuckmere Valley near the Seven Sisters Country Park Visitor Centre, but has not been recorded from the River.

23

Photographs to show the flowers in detail and the plant as it grows.

English names used in this book are from the standard English names as in the *Field Flora of the British Isles* by Stace (see book list on page 206). Latin names are the most recent ones, as used by Stace.

Wild flower protection

By appreciating wild flowers and how and where they grow, we hope that people will have an increased awareness, not just of the beauty of the countryside around them, but also its fragility. Many of the once common species listed in this book are now only found at a few locations around Sussex. This is often because of changes in land management and agricultural practice. The sites where the flowers grow are often vulnerable so please take care not to damage either the plants or the site, so that the flowers can flourish again in future years.

All wild plants are given protection under British law. Under the Wildlife and Countryside Act 1981 and later the Countryside and Rights of Way Act 2000, it is illegal to uproot any wild plant without permission from the landowner. Plants on nature reserves and nationally designated sites, (including National Nature Reserves and Sites of Special Scientific Interest) also have strong protection. It is illegal to pick, uproot or remove plants for example on Wildlife Trust nature reserves or National Trust land.

Some plants are specifically protected under Schedule 8 of the Wildlife and Countryside Act 1981. This Act provides a list of endangered plants, that are protected against intentional picking, uprooting and destruction. Schedule 8 of the Wildlife and Countryside Act is revised every five years. Current lists of the species afforded special protection in Britain are listed at www.bsbi.org.uk, the website of the Botanical Society of the British Isles.

spring

Bluebell
Hyacinthoides non-scripta

Lily family
Liliaceae

Habitat: Throughout Sussex, but especially in deciduous and mixed woodlands and in hedgebanks
Height: 20-45cm
Flowering: April and May
Status: Schedule 8,
'Look-alike' plants: Spanish Bluebell and hybrids

The shiny, green linear leaves, 20 to 35cm long, grow from a bulb in early spring, followed by a single stem which is upright when the flowers are in bud. As the flowers open the one-sided flowering spike nods at the tip so each of the four to 16 flowers is drooping giving the flower spike a graceful curve.

Each flower has two narrow bluish-green bracts where it joins the stem, and the flower which is tubular has strongly recurved tips to the sepals. The flowers are characteristically azure blue, a colour notoriously difficult to capture on photographic film. However, looking closely at the flowers shows that each has a pink line on the sepals. It is this very slight pinkish tinge that is often the photographer's downfall!

The flowers are strongly scented and pollinated by insects, but like many bulbs when grown from seed it takes many years to flower. There have been different opinions on the harm done to Bluebell populations by various methods of picking the flowers. Experiments have shown that colonies did decline if heavily picked and that whether the flowers were cut or pulled made little difference to the bulbs. However, heavy trampling of the leaves will prevent the bulbs from obtaining the necessary sugars in storage months.

Bluebell

Occasionally Bluebells have white flowers – or less often pink. However, it is the massed blue of the typical plants that is the glory of our native Bluebell. The anthers are cream-coloured, this is a particularly useful character separating our native true Bluebell from the one commonly grown in gardens, the Spanish Bluebell *Hyacinthoides hispanica*, which has purplish-blue anthers. The Spanish Bluebell is also distinguished by having an erect flower stem, and flowers that are bell-shaped but with the tips not recurved. The two Bluebell species hybridise very readily and, as is so often the case with hybrids, the resulting plants are very vigorous and spread quickly. Careful identification of Bluebells, apparently wild but growing near towns, has shown that in some areas native Bluebells in copses, rews and hedgerows not far from towns and gardens are now almost all hybrids. Fortunately in Sussex we have still some large areas of woodland and forest with true native Bluebells.

Traditionally our county and our country have been famous for the drifts of flowering Bluebells in the woods in spring. The British Isles is the centre of the distribution of this flower, so well-known to us, but rare and restricted to the western fringe of Europe, Britain, Ireland and small areas of northern Spain, the Netherlands, Belgium, north west France and north west Germany. Botanical visitors from the United States, continental Europe and many other countries come to view our Bluebells, and a blue haze of flowers under the fresh green of newly opening woodland trees is indeed a memorable sight.

Coralroot
Cardamine bulbifera

Cabbage family
Brassicaceae (Cruciferae)

Habitat: In ancient woodland, mainly near paths and along shady streams and on damp road verges
Height: 30-60cm
Flowering: April to June
Status: Nationally Scarce
'Look-alike' plants: Cuckooflower (Lady's Smock) from which Coralroot is distinguished by the purple bulbils in the axils of the upper leaves

Coralroot is a perennial with a cream-coloured, tangled rhizome (which gives the plant its name). The leaves vary up the stem, the lower leaves are pinnate with toothed leaflets, the middle stem-leaves have three leaflets and the upper a single simple leaf. Most mature plants have bulbils in the axils of these upper leaves, and flowers on some stems.

The four pinkish-purple petals are 12 to 18mm across, and the sepals are purple-tipped. The plant spreads both through its rhizome, and through its bulbils that fall when ripe and germinate in the soil beneath – some may first be carried away by ants from the parent plants. The seed pods which develop on these plants with flowers very rarely ripen in this country.

Although a Nationally Scarce plant, in north east Sussex we have one of its two British strongholds. We also have scattered sites in West Sussex, some of which have large populations (up to 2000 plants in some years). In East

Sussex we have many localities, mostly in the Mayfield, Wadhurst, Stonegate and Hurst Green areas. The Sussex Botanical Recording Society surveys in 2000, 2001 and 2002 have given us a very comprehensive knowledge of this plant's distribution in Sussex. Eight localities in West Sussex have also been studied, some of these in forest gills north of Horsham.

In England the second stronghold for Coralroot is surprisingly in a different habitat – in Beech woods on the Chilterns, contrasting with the colonies on the slightly acidic soil of the Weald clay in north east Sussex.

Some of the road verges where Coralroot grows have 'Protected for Wildlife' status. West Sussex is notable because of its Roadside Verge Project, which is part of a Habitat Action Plan.

Beyond Britain, Coralroot is known from southern Scandinavia and France to the Black Sea, also in south-west Asia and the Caucasus. Here the main colonies are on chalky soil, often in Beech woods in the mountains.

Early Meadow-grass
Poa infirma

Grass family
Graminae

Habitat: Rough ground and paths near the sea
Height: 1-12cm
Flowering: March and April
Status: Not Scarce
'Look-alike' plants: Annual Meadow-grass

A simple way to identify the meadow-grass family is by the boat-shaped tip of the leaves. Within the meadow-grass family Early Meadow-grass is distinguished from the widespread and common Annual Meadow-grass by its yellow-green colour, its smaller size and earlier flowering period, and the much smaller anthers 0.2 to 0.5mm in Early Meadow-grass (compared to 0.6 to 0.8mm of Annual Meadow-grass).

Until very recently this small annual native grass was restricted to the western half of southern England, the Channel Islands and the Isles of Scilly. The grass was first found in western Cornwall in 1876, but not seen again until 1950, when it was found at the Lizard and in the Isles of Scilly. In the last ten years it has been recorded from Dorset and Hampshire.

The first record for West Sussex was in 1998 and the first for East Sussex was in 2000. Since these first sightings in the counties the Sussex Botanical Recording Society has organised field meetings along the coast early in the year to search diligently for this grass, and can now claim seven West Sussex sites and nine in East Sussex. During the year 2000 the rarity status of this species in Sussex passed from rare to scarce and then to locally frequent. Possibly this dramatic increase and spread of this small grass could be linked to global warming.

Early Spider-orchid
Ophrys sphegodes

Orchid family
Orchidaceae

Habitat: South facing chalk
grassland close to the sea
Height: 5-15cm
Flowering: Late April to mid-May
Status: *Red Data Book* (Lower
Risk, near threatened) Schedule 8
'Look-alike' plants: Bee Orchid
and Late Spider-orchid

This little orchid is one of an attractive
group of orchids whose flowers mimic
insects thus inviting the pollinators to
visit. The three to four grey-green lower leaves are short and broad forming
a loose rosette, and have distinct parallel veins. It is not unusual for the leaf-
tips to be browned by late spring frosts. The upper leaves clasp the stem and
also have well-marked veins. The yellow-green sepals are roughly oblong with
slightly wavy margins and the tip of the top sepal curves forward over the top
of the flower. There are two yellow-green upper petals that are short and
straight. The lip is round, convex and a warm rich brown in colour, velvety in
texture and marked quite clearly in the centre with a blue-grey smooth
irregular 'H'. In the centre of the flower is the specialised orchid family
'column' with the stigma and stamens, and in the Early Spider-orchid this is
shaped like a bird's head.

The earliest Sussex record of Early Spider-orchid was from Pyecombe in
1834 and in the 1930s the orchid was also recorded in West Sussex near
Saddlescombe. However, it has not been found in West Sussex in the past 70
years and is now presumed to be extinct there. In East Sussex there are ten
recent sites, almost all on the Downs close to the sea, such as at Castle Hill
National Nature Reserve and Bullock Down, and on cliff-top turf at Belle Tout
and Cow Gap.

Early Spider-orchid

Early in May is the time to search for this often very tiny orchid, remembering that it is mainly yellow-green in colour and so easily overlooked; worse still it can be very easily trampled – so careful 'feet-watching' is essential. The number of flowers varies greatly from year to year at different sites in the Castle Hill Reserve where it is carefully monitored: 10,000 plants have been estimated, of which about 1,500 will flower in a good year. Most of the other Sussex colonies have a small number of plants which may be scattered in the turf.

As one of the insect-mimicking *Ophrys* orchids, the Early Spider-orchid flower has a good resemblance to a fat hairy garden spider. Amazingly the similarity is not only from the pattern and the velvety texture of the lip, but the flower has also a scent similar to that of the mimicked spider. Of the other 'look-alike' orchids in this group the Late Spider-orchid has pink sepals and flowers later. However there has only been one record for this plant in Sussex, near Edburton, and it was never refound. More common is the Bee Orchid; this also has pink sepals, the lip pattern differs and the central column (also like a bird's head) is stouter than that of Early Spider-orchid. The Bee Orchid is found in similar habitats, but is more widespread on the Downs and in chalky roadside verges and rough ground.

In England the Early Spider-orchid is very local and only found from east Kent and west Suffolk to Dorset and west Gloucestershire. It is known in central and southern Europe, and in the Near East.

Green Hellebore
Helleborus viridis

Buttercup family
Ranunculaceae

Habitat: Damp woodlands
on calcareous soils
Height: 20-35cm
Flowering: March and April
Status: Scarce in Sussex
'Look-alike' plants:
Stinking Hellebore
(see page 22)

Green Hellebore is a short stout native perennial, growing from a rhizome with a stem that is often blackish at the base. The plants do not overwinter (a distinction from the Stinking Hellebore), and are most often leafless below the lowest branch of the stem at the time of flowering. The lower leaves are long-stalked with seven to 11 narrow segments with toothed margins and prominent veins on the paler lower surface; the stem leaves are similar, but smaller and stalkless, and the bracts below the flowers are deeply divided. The two to four drooping flowers have pale green sepals 3.5cm across, open and saucer-shaped. The tiny flowers in the centre develop into three broad fruiting and beaked capsules, which are long persistent.

The Green Hellebore has always been rare in Sussex, but it is now much reduced in both counties. It grows mostly in damp Beech woods on the chalk

Green Hellebore

Downs and by streams fed by chalk springs. We have nine post-1986 records of which the West Sussex colonies at Lordington and Sutton are persistent and have been known for many years. It is also in gardens, and occasionally escapes becoming naturalised nearby. The distinguishing features of the two hellebores are summarised in the table below.

	Green Hellebore	Stinking Hellebore
Odour	No foetid smell	Foetid smell when fresh and crushed
Foliage	Stem lasting only from winter to late spring and no overwintering leaves	Leaves and stem overwintering from spring to spring
Flowers	Two to four flowers only, saucer shaped and pale green	Many-flowered, cup-shaped flowers with purple rim

Both these hellebores had the old name of Bear's-foot from the shape of their leaves. Green Hellebore is native to Central Europe, from Spain to north west France, Switzerland and Hungary.

Heath Dog-violet
Viola canina

Violet family
Violaceae

Habitat: Dry or wet heaths, and leached areas in chalk grassland
Height: 2-10cm
Flowering: April to June
Status: Scarce in Sussex
'Look-alike' plants: Other wild violets such as Common Dog-violet and Hairy Violet

The Heath Dog-violet is a perennial without a central non-flowering rosette; instead the leaves all grow on sprawling stems. In Sussex it is most often a neat, compact low plant, flowering in spring – but later than the Common Dog-violet. The stalked leaves are bright or dark green, rather thick, oval to triangular with a heart-shaped base and with bluntly toothed edges. The flowers can vary in colour from pale to deep blue, but usually with a conspicuous greenish-yellow short, thick, blunt spur. The sepals are narrow and pointed with a lobe at the base. The flowers are not scented, the reason for the derogatory name of 'Dog' Violet, meaning that it is not a true scented violet.

In Sussex the Heath Dog-violet has always been uncommon, due to lack of suitable habitats. It requires a fairly open heath-like habitat where it will not be overgrown, as Dog-violet is easily crowded out. There are nearly a dozen sites for this plant in Sussex. Five are located in West Sussex: the cricket outfield at Westbourne, short turf at Ebernoe and Easebourne and the grounds of Parham Park. It also grows on the Downs at Bignor Hill, on the highest point where the chalk has been leached (or percolated through by the rain) from the soil surface therefore neutralising the soil. In East Sussex

spring

Heath Dog-violet

there are six recent records, including Castle Hill National Nature Reserve, Holtye Common Golf Course, Seddlescombe Heath and Seaford Head Golf Course. The number of plants has decreased considerably in the last 20 years so it is now listed as Scarce in Sussex to ensure that it is monitored.

There are records throughout the British Isles, where it also grows on sand dunes and in fens. Beyond Britain it grows in Europe from Iceland and Scandinavia to central Spain (but not in western France or Portugal), northern Italy, Montenegro and Bulgaria and also northern Asia to Kamchatka and Manchuria.

Italian Lords-and-Ladies
Arum italicum ssp. *neglectum*

Arum family
Araceae

Habitat: In light shade often on stony, chalky ground, under shrubs or brambles on chalk
Height: 20-30cm
Flowering: Late April to May
Status: Scarce in Britain but with many records in West Sussex
'Look-alike' plants: Lords-and-Ladies and the garden form of Italian Lords-and-Ladies, which has whitish leaf veins.

This perennial plant grows from a tuber, with arrow shaped leaves that are 15 to 25cm long. The flowering spathe overtopping the leaves is a clear pale green, never spotted, often bent forward at the tip, and the central yellow spadix about a third of the length of the spathe.

When conditions of light and warmth are just right, pale green tightly furled spathes are seen emerging from clumps of leaves; these gradually open to reveal the spadix. When the flower parts hidden at the base of the spadix are ready for pollination, a smell (foetid to us but very attractive to midges) is produced bringing midges from long distances to the flowers. Twenty to 30 midges, (although as many as 4,000 midges have been recorded on one spadix!) remain trapped overnight in the bulbous capsule below the spadix, but fly off in the morning when the flowers are pollinated and the barrier of hairs that had trapped them withers. In late summer conspicuous scarlet berries are a favourite food for Mistle Thrushes and other birds; however, these berries are poisonous to humans.

The Italian Lords-and-Ladies is not hardy and in England is found only near the south coast, south of a line below which snow lies for less than five days in a year. It is, as its name suggests, widespread in western and southern Europe, where in many areas it is the dominant member of the Arum family and our Common Lords-and-Ladies does not occur. In Sussex it shows a warmer western distribution, with the most eastern colony at Coombes near Lancing.

Italian Lords-and-Ladies can most easily be distinguished from the Common Lords-and-Ladies of our hedgerows by the earlier appearance of its leaves. Often in October, or by mid-November, the leaves of Italian Lords-and-Ladies are through the soil and unfurled; leaves of the common species appear a few weeks later, even in a mild autumn. The garden form is similar, but has yellow or white veins in the leaves.

In Elizabethan times washerwomen used the starch from the tubers to stiffen the fancy ruffs worn by the men at that time. Italian Lords-and-Ladies was much sought after by the washerwomen as these tubers contain fewer needle calcium oxalate crystals than the tubers of our common species – so the rare species left their hands less sore and reddened. Italian Lords-and-Ladies has been well-studied, with a whole book written on the fascination of the Lords-and-Ladies species. More recent studies on the distribution of Italian Lords-and-Ladies in West Sussex were published in 1998 by Sussex Botanical Recording Society members (see page 209).

Italian Lords-and-Ladies is found in quantity along Mill Road, Arundel.

Stinking Hellebore
Helleborus foetidus

Buttercup family
Ranunculaceae

Habitat: Woodlands and hedgerows mainly on chalky soils – also from gardens
Height: 20-80cm
Flowering: February to April
Status: Nationally Scarce and Scarce in Sussex
'Look-alike' plants: Green Hellebore (see page 16) and garden forms of Stinking Hellebore

This short-lived perennial has overwintering stems, that are blackish below. There are no basal leaves, but dark green evergreen lower stem leaves, long-stalked and with three to nine narrow pointed toothed leaves. The unusually shaped leaves give the hellebores their Old English name of Bear's Foot. The middle stem leaves have enlarged sheaths, and the many flowers have broadly oval sepals 1 to 3cm across, almost globular and cup-shaped, and drooping. These foetid, yellowish-green flowers are bordered with a reddish-purple margin.

Stinking Hellebore spreads entirely by seed and the tiny central flowers are pollinated by early bees and other insects; the seed capsules are open so that the ripe seeds drop and are then dispersed by ants and snails.

This unusual-looking plant is grown in many gardens, along with its relatives such as Christmas or London Roses. It readily escapes from cultivation and naturalises from seed in suitable chalk areas. In

Stinking Hellebore

East Sussex it is rare and not considered to be native, but in West Sussex there are old records from 1876 of long-standing colonies from woods around Arundel and Houghton and these can be seen today.

Stinking and Green Hellebores were used in medicine and veterinary cures. For humans they are dangerously toxic if the dosage is even slightly miscalculated. It was used at one time for worms in children; Gilbert White (1720-93) wrote *"where it killed not the patient it would certainly kill worms; but the worst of it is that it will sometimes kill both"*. In the 18th century a *'quantity of roots'* was sent to Guy's Hospital for medical use – probably increasing the rarity of these plants. Their use in medicine has thankfully long been discontinued.

Stinking Hellebore grows in Europe from Belgium to Germany, Spain and Italy and as far south as Morocco. It is abundant in the mountain Beech woods of the Spanish Pyrenees. The plants cultivated in our gardens are forms of this species from southern and eastern Europe.

Toothwort

Lathraea squamaria

Broomrape family
Orobanchaceae

Habitat: Woods and
hedgerows
Height: 8-18cm
Flowering: March and April
Status: Scarce in Sussex
'Look-alike' plants: Some
broomrapes and the Bird's-
nest Orchid, but all these
flower in mid to late summer

Toothwort is a perennial parasitic plant. It has no green leaves with chlorophyll, instead it grows on the roots of woody shrubs or trees, most often Hazel, Elm or Elder, and obtains the necessary nutrition from the host plant through the roots.

The plant has a stout, unbranched flowering shoot which (having no chlorophyll) is pale pink or white. The shoots are above the woodland soil in early spring, often before the main leaf coverage is on the trees and the woodland floor is only lightly shaded. The flower shoots have a few whitish scales held against the stem below, and the 12 to 20 flowers grow from one side of the stem above. The stems droop at first and finally become upright as the top buds open.

The two-lipped flowers are sometimes purple, but more often a pale pinkish-cream, and each has a broadly oval bract. The white sepals are glandular, hairy and tubular with four broadly triangular teeth. The colouring of these plants tones well with dead sticks and pale oak leaves on the bare woodland floor in early spring. The flowers are visited by Bumble-bees, and the following capsules are oval and pointed.

spring

24

Toothwort

Toothwort is a rare plant in Sussex, except in a few scattered localities. We have eight recent sites for Toothwort of which only one is found in the east near Hastings. There are good colonies in the far west of West Sussex and in woods near Christ's Hospital near Horsham. In Sussex almost all Toothwort grows on the roots of Hazel bushes, and you need to be out early in the year to see the flowers.

The name Toothwort comes from the plant's resemblance to a row of teeth on a jaw. This is particularly obvious when the plant is in fruit. The fruit capsules are ivory-white and shiny, and often channelled like teeth. Some old medical herbals have fine engravings of the fruiting Toothwort looking distinctly like teeth. At the end of the 14th century the value of many medicinal plants became based on what is known as the *Doctrine of Signatures*. This taught that the healing herbs were signposted by God in some way for man's guidance – so as to show what disease or part of the body the plant could be used for. For example, because of this resemblance to teeth the 'Toothwort' was used to 'cure' toothache, and sometimes the treatment and care did indeed ease the toothache. The idea was developed by Swiss alchemist and physician Paracelsus (1490-1541) and was very popular with the Puritans. Much earlier the herbalists of ancient Greece thought of it as 'sympathetic' magic.

Found in all of Britain except the far north, and throughout Europe and western Asia to the Himalayas.

Yew

Taxus baccata

Yew family
Taxaceae

Habitat: Woods and scrub, mainly on chalk. Often planted, especially in churchyards
Height: To 20m
Flowering: March and April; fruiting August and September
Status: Not Scarce
'Look-alike' plants: Cultivated Yews *Taxus* species

In West Sussex we have the largest Yew forest in Europe at Kingley Vale. This is a National Nature Reserve north of Chichester, where Yew trees are dominant in some 400 acres. Yews thrive better than other trees on steep chalk downland slopes, especially those facing south and west.

The distinctive trees can produce leafy branches from stumps or old trunks. The thin, scaly bark is reddish-brown and the twigs are green with short stalked leaves 1 to 3cm long, which are very dark green above and a yellowish-green below. The midrib is prominent on both sides, with a pointed tip and the leaf margins inrolled. The very poisonous seed is enclosed in a clear scarlet non-poisonous fleshy cover or 'aril' about 6mm long. Dead Yew wood can be recognised by breaking a twig, which has a strong scent of lead pencils.

At Kingley Vale there are many old gnarled trees, some 500 years or more, and it is an experience to walk under the cathedral-like arching branches. To the Victorians the vale was a "*sinister and fantastic forest*" but a past warden describes the trees as "*wild and hoary with age*".

The Yew has immense history and for many centuries the trees supplied the wood for Britain's strategic weapon, the longbow. Richard III ordered a general planting of Yews for use by archers in 1483 and Elizabeth I encouraged

Yew

the planting of Yews in churchyards where they could be kept from poisoning grazing animals, and the trees could be cared for.

Away from Kingley Vale many of the Yew tree records today are in churchyards, with famous Sussex Yews in Walberton and Easebourne. The leaves and seeds of the Yew are known to be very poisonous, but, as with many poisons in small and controlled doses, it can be used medicinally; taxol was given as a remedy for some cancers, and for a time churches could sell clippings from their Yew trees to drug companies. The fleshy red aril around the seed has long been known as non-toxic, indeed the herbalist Gerard (1636) describes eating the aril without harm *"when I was yonge and went to schoole, divers of my schoole fellows and likewise myself did eat our fils of this tree"* – but the aril is too close to the toxic seed for casual experimentation.

A visit to Kingley Vale can be recommended to see the Yews, as well as ancient downland turf, a variety of wildlife and mounds from a Bronze Age settlement. The burial mounds on the skyline are known locally as the Devil's Humps.

The Yew is native to Britain and Ireland – local though often common in England, Wales and Ireland, but very rare in Scotland. It is found wild in most countries of Europe from Scandinavia to north Africa and east to the Crimea and the western Himalayas.

early summer

Bastard Balm
Melittis melissophyllum

Dead-nettle family
Lamiaceae

Habitat: Hedgerows and field edges
Height: 30-60cm
Flowering: May to July
Status: Nationally Scarce and Scarce in Sussex
'Look-alike' plants: The large flowers distinguish Bastard Balm from other members of the family, except perhaps for the larger-flowered Hemp-nettle

The term 'bastard' used in this flower's name comes not from the old English meaning of the word 'an inferior kind of' but 'having the appearance of' as it is not the true balm used in herbal medicine. This related Balm *Melissa officinalis* was the official drug, an infusion of which made a pleasant and cooling tea for feverish patients, and when fresh it is lemon-scented. Bastard Balm is also aromatic, although with a stronger less pleasant scent, but superficially the leaves are similar to Balm.

Unlike Bastard Balm, Balm is an introduced plant widely grown in herb gardens, and occasionally found naturalised as a garden escape, as in Amberley village. Bastard Balm, however, is a native species. It has leaves that are broadly oval and stalked, 5 to 8cm long and with rounded marginal teeth. The distinctive flowers are in whorls of two to six, and double-lipped. The upper lip has two to three teeth and is slightly concave, and the lower lip has two rounded lobes. The petals can be white, deep rose-pink or white splodged with pink, and these variations are often regional. There is a significant quantity of nectar at the base of the petal tube, attracting insects such as Bumble-bees and Hawkmoths while the flower is in bloom. The sepals remain open in fruit showing the four smooth oval nutlets. In Sussex the plants have pink and white flowers.

In West Sussex we have one long-established site for Bastard Balm at Plummers Plain and here the plants are monitored. Recent sightings from

Bastard Balm

walls in Chichester are thought to be escapes from cultivation, as it is grown in gardens. Indeed, in days before conservation needs were known or necessary, some of the Bastard Balm plants in cottage gardens had been brought in from the wild.

In Britain Bastard Balm is mainly a plant of the south west, where it can still be abundant in coppiced woodlands, especially in Cornwall where many of the colonies are pink-flowered. It has disappeared from most of the sites in eastern and central England, and our West Sussex site is now the most eastern locality for Bastard Balm in Britain. It grows in central and southern Europe eastwards to Lithuania and central Ukraine. In the Julian Alps in Slovenia the Bastard Balm is common in sub-alpine woodland, with snow-white flowers.

Bastard-toadflax

Thesium humifusum

Sandalwood family
Santalaceae

Habitat: Short chalk downland turf
Height: Spreading prostrate and trailing stems,
 2.5-5cm long
Flowering: June to August
Status: Nationally Scarce
'Look-alike' plants: Bastard-toadflax is quite
distinctive with yellow-green trailing stems and
minute flowers

This tiny, almost prostrate yellow-green plant is semi-parasitic. It does have leaves, but the roots also attach to the roots of other species in the downland habitat to steal their nutrients. It has opposite, linear leaves with only one vein growing on slender weakly spreading stems edged with rough angles. The yellowish flower stalks are short and stout, with two or three narrow bracteoles at the junction with the main stem. The tiny 3mm flowers have five petals, yellowish-green outside and whitish inside. The 3mm oval ribbed fruit develops in late summer and is crowned by the remains of the flowers. Rather noticeably the seeds appear like wrinkled buds.

Bastard-toadflax is listed as Nationally Scarce as it has been lost from older sites due to ploughing of downland and more intensive farming. In Sussex it has long been considered as rare. It is often inconspicuous growing in the grass and sharp eyes are needed to spot the plants in the turf. In Sussex we have had a large number of active botanists since the 1960s, and consequently more sites have been identified. We now have 20 sites recorded since 1978, ten in East Sussex and ten in West Sussex. These include Kingley Vale National Nature Reserve, Arundel Park, near the old cement works at Upper Beeding, near Tenant Hill at Edburton, and Southwick Hill in West Sussex. In East Sussex it is found at Beachy Head, Seven Sisters, Mount Caburn, Itford Hill near Southease and Beacon Hill at Ovingdean.

Bastard-toadflax

This plant was thought by early botanists to be in the toadflax family. However when it was discovered that it was not a true toadflax it became known as the 'Bastard' Toadflax.

In Europe this species is confined to Belgium, France, Britain and Ireland, the Netherlands and Spain; it also has a southern Atlantic seaboard distribution. In mountainous areas of Europe there are many other *Thesium* species, but *Thesium humifusum* is the only representative of the sandalwood family growing in the British Isles.

Burnt Orchid (Burnt-tip Orchid)

Orchis ustulata

Orchid family
Orchidaceae

Habitat: Old chalk downland and unimproved chalk pastures
Height: 6-12cm
Flowering: Early May to mid June, and late July
Status: Nationally Scarce and Scarce in Sussex
'Look-alike' plants: This orchid is distinctive

This miniature orchid with its distinctive colouring is a delight to find, but it is sadly becoming rarer. Often growing in small clumps, Burnt Orchid stems have two to five broad-grooved leaves 2 to 3cm long with well-marked parallel veins. Several of these leaves sheath the stem. The flower spikes are dense and cylindrical, each flower having a neat 'hood' formed by the sepals and small, narrow upper petals. The lip is white and dotted with crimson spots, and has a 'long' 5 to 6mm narrow central lobe with a shallow notch at the tip. At the base of the lip, extending backwards from the flower towards the stem, is a short down-curving conical spur and below each flower a small pointed reddish-brown bract. The unopened flower buds are dark maroon giving the top of the flower spike the appearance of having been burnt – and providing the orchid with its English and scientific names.

The Burnt Orchid grows very slowly from seed to maturity and eventual flowering. As with all orchids the seed needs an association with a specific fungus in the soil in order to germinate. For the Burnt Orchid it may take as long as ten years before the first shoot and leafy stem appears above the soil after germination and it may be several more years before the plant flowers. Ploughing obviously disturbs this cycle and Burnt Orchids can only survive in 'unimproved' pastures or old downland.

Burnt Orchid (Burnt-tip Orchid)

This orchid is variable in its flowering habits: In some years it may appear in large numbers but in others very few flower at the same site. The two distinct flowering times, often four to six weeks apart, is unusual and has led to intensive studies of the plants. It is thought that orchids from the two flowering periods are quite distinct.

In West Sussex there is now only one site for the Burnt Orchid, but in East Sussex we have more than ten sites. These are downland locations from Beachy Head, Coombe Bottom near Cuckmere, Combe Hill near Willingdon and Lullington Heath National Nature Reserve. It is also found at Cradle Hill near Seaford, Mount Caburn National Nature Reserve in Glynde and at Castle Hill National Nature Reserve. It has also been found at Oxteddle Bottom, part of the Sussex Wildlife Trust Malling Downs nature reserve.

The Burnt Orchid has a few scattered sites in northern England, and in Wiltshire there are still some good-sized populations. It is found in central Europe northwards to southern Scandinavia, south to the Mediterranean – and east to beyond the Urals. In the eastern Alps the plants are sometimes taller and more robust.

Cat-mint (Catnep, Catnip)

Nepeta cataria

Dead-nettle family
Lamiaceae

Habitat: Pathsides and scrub grassland on chalk Downs
Height: 40-70cm
Flowering: June to September
Status: Scarce in Sussex
'Look-alike' plants: Calamint species

These very aromatic plants are soft, grey-woolly perennials with erect stems and oval toothed leaves that are heart-shaped at the base. The lower leaves are stalked and about 4cm long. The whorls of white flowers with small purple spots are densely crowded into a terminal flower-head, with some lower whorls more spaced down the stem. The double-lipped flowers with a short tube are about 12mm high and the sepals below are downy, lance shaped and pointed. The three upper petals have longer teeth than the two lower ones. The flowers are pollinated by bees, producing four smooth oval nutlet fruits.

In Sussex Cat-mint has always been rare as a wild plant, and there are less than ten sites where this plant is known. Some of these are almost certainly garden escapes. In West Sussex there are records from the edge of the Dyke Golf course at Ewe Bottom and in Brighton it is found on walls and under bushes in Preston Park. In East Sussex it occurs in downland scrub on Itford Hill, and a well-known site at Gap Bottom, Crowlink.

Cat-mint (Catnep, Catnip)

The leaves of these plants have been used in medicine, as a digestive and a tonic given as a tea, and they are also said to have psychoactive effects similar to cannabis. Many gardeners grow Cat-mint and it is particularly well known that the plant is irresistible to most cats. Over 62 chemicals have been isolated from *Nepeta cataria*. Of these it is Nepetalactone which is the feliphile, loved by cats. This has the potent ability to excite cats and other Felidae including lions and jaguars (but, not tigers!). Cats have a genetically sensitised response to Nepetalactone that can cause them to behave in a drug induced manner. The chemical responsible is also similar to a pheromone associated with courtship in cats.

Some of the garden Cat-mints are similar species or hybrids, and in the USA and New Zealand *Nepeta cataria* is called Catnip. It is also said to be rabbit-proof as a cultivated ornamental.

Wild Cat-mint has scattered records in England and Wales and in Jersey, but it is rare in Ireland. In Europe it grows from Scandinavia to Portugal, Spain, Corsica, Sicily, and Greece; also in western and central Asia to Kashmir. It is naturalised in North America, South Africa and New Zealand.

Chaffweed

Anagallis minima

Primrose family
Primulaceae

Habitat: Woodland rides and paths on damp sandy soils
Height: Stems up to 5cm
Flowering: June to August
Status: Not yet scarce – apparently decreasing but possibly overlooked
'Look-alike' plants: Blinks and Rupturewort

Many attractive wild flowers are colourful and obvious, but there is also a special fascination in the miniature, inconspicuous plants for which a search is necessary, often on hands and knees! The flowers of these tiny plants are frequently exquisite in design and rewarding to find. To fully see their intricate detail a magnifying lens, or a photographic enlargement may be needed.

The smooth, hairless leaves of Chaffweed are rounded oval and from 3 to 5mm long, with those on the upper parts of the stem arranged alternately. The tiny solitary flowers grow on the stems without stalks, each at the base of the leaf, and the very pale pink or sometimes white petals are overtopped by the longer sepals. The flowers are followed by tiny, round seed capsules, which are green and flushed pink, appearing like little apples and when found at this stage the plants are distinctive.

In Sussex we have over a dozen recent sites, mainly on rides in woodland along the forest ridge through central Sussex. There is, however, a reduction in the number of sites where it is found; this decrease may possibly be due to the drainage of some habitats and forest felling, it could also be that the little plant has sometimes been overlooked.

Chaffweed grows in most countries of central Europe, but not in the far north or far south of the continent.

Chamomile

Chamaemelum nobile

Daisy family
Asteraceae

Habitat: A plant of heaths and grazed commons that is also found on village greens and cricket pitches
Height: 6-16cm
Flowering: June and July
Status: Nationally Scarce and Scarce in Sussex
'Look-alike' plants: Mayweed and Corn Chamomile

This aromatic herb is a low, much-branched, creeping plant with hairy flowering stems. The leaves are 1.5 to 5cm long, deeply and finely dissected. The flower-heads are 18 to 25mm across, long-stalked, with each flower standing alone. The scales below the flowers have papery white edges. The white petalled flowers have yellow centres, and the outer florets turn back as the flowers age, with the central disc of tubular yellow florets elongating to a conical centre.

Chamomile is native to sandy heaths and grassy places in England, Wales and Ireland, and locally frequent in the Channel Islands. In Sussex, and south east England in general, Chamomile has decreased as these habitats have decreased. This is largely due to changes in farming practice since the Second World War which meant that open heathlands were no longer included in grazing regimes. When heathland is abandoned it soon becomes overgrown with scrub and eventually reverts to woodland. Grazing animals on village greens are also no longer part of country life.

However, during the 1990s surveys and special searches for Chamomile were organised and several new sites in Sussex were discovered. It was found that cricket pitches and recreation grounds provide ideal conditions for Chamomile, with frequent mowing and trampling recreating the grazing regimes of the past. Chamomile is not always popular with groundsmen as, in dry seasons, when the grassy turf yellows, it stands out as dark green patches

Chamomile

giving a mottled appearance to their swards. But look out for Chamomile when watching cricket at Westbourne, Heyshott, Petworth, Lurgashall, Ebernoe, Slinfold, Staplefield, Upperton, Henfield or Oaklands Park, Chichester. The Chamomile on Staplefield village green was found after a conversation with the school teacher who had smelt the distinctive scent when her pupils were playing cricket.

Chamomile has for many years been planted to make a scented lawn. A famous one is in Buckingham Palace Gardens, and in East Sussex, Buxted Park has a Chamomile lawn. When planting for lawns a non-flowering clone may be used to lessen the need for frequent mowing. Chamomile is also used as a herbal tea and as a medicinal herb, these are mainly derived from the double-flowered variety *flore-pleno*. The flowers are picked off in July and August when the bracts are still green and the white ray florets are just beginning to bend backwards. Gerard noted in his *Herbal* in 1597 that Chamomile "*is a speciall helpe against wearisomenesse, it easeth and mitigateth pain, it mollifieth and suppleth*". The tea can be made from fresh or dried flowers and these are also used in shampoo and skin preparations.

Chamomile grows in Western Europe from Belgium southwards, in north Africa and the Azores.

Childing Pink

Petrorhagia nanteuilii

Pink family
Caryophyllaceae

Habitat: On shingle, coastal sand, and dry grassy places close to the sea
Height: 10-40cm
Flowering: Late June to July (occasionally flowers into August and early September)
Status: Red Data Book, (Endangered) Schedule 8, and Scarce in Sussex
'Look-alike' plants: Maiden Pink

The only sites in Britain for this endangered *Red Data Book* species, which is legally protected by Schedule 8 of the Wildlife and Countryside Act, 1981, are now in West Sussex and Hampshire, mostly around Pagham Harbour, with one recent record from the sand dunes at Shoreham. Good colonies have recently been found in Hampshire.

The Childing Pink is a slender grey-green annual with a wiry stem and narrow, paired leaves 1 to 2cm long at intervals up the stem. At the top of the stem the small pink open flowers are 6 to 8mm across with notched petals, and they flower one each day from a small dense ovoid head of brownish papery bracts which holds one to 11 flower buds.

The populations of Childing Pink fluctuate considerably from year to year. As a plant that flourishes in a Mediterranean climate with mild wet winters but hot dry summers, Childing Pink requires warmth in late July and August to ripen the seeds and ensure good colonies in the following year.

The Childing Pink populations at Pagham and Church Norton in West Sussex have been studied, monitored and counted for some years now. The number of plants has varied from tens of thousands in good years, to small colonies of just a few plants with some colonies not appearing at all. The Childing Pink could be threatened by natural erosion, shingle movement or coastal defence works, as well as cool summers. Many of the good colonies are in the Pagham Harbour Local Nature Reserve where the Warden can

Childing Pink

give information about finding the plants.

In Jersey the Childing Pink is still common, and also in Spain and Portugal, where unlike other areas it is common inland as well as on the coast.

It is scattered in coastal habitats in France, Italy, Corsica, Sardinia and the Balearic Islands. Childing Pink also grows in Morocco, Canary Islands and Madeira.

Corn Marigold

Chrysanthemum segetum

Daisy family
Asteraceae

Habitat: An arable weed of acid soils
Height: 20-30cm
Flowering: June to August
Status: Scarce in Sussex
'Look-alike' plants: Garden Marigold

Corn Marigold is an annual with simple or branched stems. The leaves are hairless, blue-green and somewhat fleshy, oblong, 2 to 8cm long and the lower leaves are lobed with a winged stalk. The flower heads are 3.5 to 6.5cm across, solitary and on a long stalk which is thickened at the top. The bracts below the petals have broad, pale brown papery margins. The ring of petals is broad and golden yellow, and the central disc of tubular florets is also yellow.

The cheerful yellow daisy flowers of this plant are very appealing. It was once widespread in East and West Sussex, and in the 1990s it was still occasionally abundant in the sandy areas around Wiggonholt and Cootham. However, there has been a 90 percent loss of Sussex sites for this plant in the last 20 years.

The steep decline in this flower's incidence as an arable weed is due to modern agricultural methods, but the seeds are long lived in the soil and there is always the chance of finding some plants in newly turned ground. Occasionally plants from wild flower seed mixtures appear in re-seeded

44

Corn Marigold

areas, but these are unlikely to persist unless the area is frequently ploughed to provide the 'cultivation' required by this species.

Corn Marigold was often called 'Gold' or 'Gouldes', but in the days of older farming methods when the plant was common it was a troublesome weed. The country people in those days had very mixed feelings about the Corn Marigold. The bright, golden, scented flowers were made into midsummer garlands and hung on their houses. At the same time it was also a particularly problematic weed which in 1523 grew commonly "*in barley and peas*". It was described as "*a loathly weed*" by Grigson, and he details the court rolls of the 14th century ordering the tenants to "*uproot a certain plant called Gold*". The plants were only slightly lessened in number by liming the fields. In 1809 William Pitt listed Corn Marigold as one of the worst weeds of arable land at that time.

Until relatively recent times cornfields, were bright with wild flowers of which Corn Marigold was one, together with Cornflower, Corncockle and many other flowers – all of which set prolific seed, enabling the plants to grow in large patches through the crops. The weeds were reintroduced through the farming methods of the times as described by Shakespeare in *Coriolanus* "*the cockle of rebellion . . . which we ourselves have plough'd for, sow'd and scattered*".

The Corn Marigold was anciently introduced to Britain, probably from western Asia, and as the plant has been found in Scottish ancient Neolithic deposits, the Corn Marigold probably arrived in Britain with neolithic agriculture. Thought to be a native of the Mediterranean region and western Asia, it is now well established throughout Europe and has also been introduced to North and South America and northern Africa.

Corncockle

Agrostemma githago

Pink family
Caryophyllaceae

Habitat: Formerly a weed of cornfields; now a casual, mainly from bird seed
Height: To 1m
Flowering: May to August
Status: Scarce in Sussex
'Look-alike' plants: Red Campion, Ragged-Robin

This colourful cornfield weed was in the past abundant in Britain, but since the 1970s it has been considered as extinct in the wild. In Sussex it was last seen established in a cornfield near Brighton in 1938.

Since 1986 there have only been eight sightings of Corncockle in Sussex. These include about 100 plants found on a mound of dumped earth on a roadside west of Billingshurst in 2002. So it is well worth keeping a look out for these attractive open rosy-pink flowers, 3 to 5cm across (described in old *Herbals* as, "*as broad as a groat*") and the petals marked inside with ten darker veins.

The old Sussex name was Puck Needles (from Puck the Goblin), as the long points of the green sepals extend between and far beyond the bright petals. These points or 'needles' readily distinguish the Corncockle from other pink wild flowers, such as Red Campion or Ragged-Robin.

Corncockle

The plant is native to the eastern Mediterranean, but through the centuries has been introduced as a weed of cultivation throughout Europe. In the second half of the last century Corncockle seeds have been sifted from the seed corn before sowing, and the plants disappeared as a weed within a few years. As far back as the 16th century the old herbals described the Corncockle, Gerard referring to plants in the crops spoiling the "*colour, taste and wholesomeness*" of the bread baked from the corn.

While, disappearing from our fields like many arable 'weeds', Corncockle is still rather common in corn in eastern Europe. In Sussex it can be seen occasionally, but mostly as a casual wayside plant. Today it is usually introduced with bird seed, or in re-seeding projects when wild flower mixes from the Continent have been used. Two recent sightings, at Woodingdean and Glynde, were in arable fields, but these did not persist beyond one year. Another recent sighting occurred where soil from a poultry farm had been used in roadworks. The Corncockle seed had originated from the commercial bird feed fed to the chickens.

Cornflower (Bluebottle)

Centaurea cyanus

Daisy family
Asteraceae

Habitat: Formerly a cornfield weed
Height: 20-90cm
Flowering: July to September
Status: Red Data Book (Endangered)
'Look-alike' plants: The larger Perennial Cornflower in gardens

The Cornflower is an annual or overwintering plant with a wiry grooved cottony stem, sometimes with slender branches. The lower leaves are stalked and between 10 and 20cm long and usually with narrow distant lobes. The upper leaves are smaller, narrow and greyish. The flower heads are 1.5 to 3cm across, with a single bloom at the top of each stem. The bracts below the flowers are green, with silvery white outer bracts. The large outer florets of the flower are bright blue, with those in the centre smaller and purple-red. The anthers are purple and the flowers are popular with both flies and bees.

The loss of Cornflowers from cornfields has been described by Geoffrey Grigson as "*one glory of colour has gone out of the English scene*" and John Clare the poet wrote 200 years ago " *. . . the blue Cornbottles crowding their splendid colours in large sheets over the land and troubling the cornfields with destroying beauty*". Fifty years ago in Britain our corn seed started to be more thoroughly sifted and 'cleaned'. The seeds of common arable 'weeds' like the Cornflower being removed from the wheat that was to be sown. As a result the Cornflower quickly dwindled to extinction, but at that time it was still possible to see it "*by the acre in French cornfields*". But in such quantities they were, in spite of their beauty, to the farmer, a troublesome weed!

Cornflower (Bluebottle)

The Cornflower has long been grown as a garden plant and was a favourite in cottage gardens with its deep blue colour and unusually shaped petals. There have been regular reports of occasional sightings of Cornflowers as casual wayside plants that have escaped from gardens, bird seed or wild flower seed mixtures. Recently with more organic farming, especially on the big estates, and less use of herbicide sprays, there are a few records of small clumps of Cornflowers in corn – mostly persisting for only one year. Two of these records were in wheat at The Burgh at Amberley

Mount, West Sussex, one in wheat at Iden in East Sussex and there was also one reported in a flax field near Lodsworth. Interestingly there are also some recent Cornflower records from newly disturbed ground at sites of past cornfields. These are likely to be from seeds which have been dormant for many years.

Cornflowers were once widespread in Britain, mainly in the south and east. Its decline and loss has been the most rapid of any plant in the British flora. It also grows throughout Europe and other parts of the world where cereal crops are grown.

Cranberry
Vaccinium oxycoccus

Heather family
Ericaceae

Habitat: In peat bogs, with Sphagnum moss
Height: 3-4cm
Flowering: June to August,
Fruiting: August to October
Status: Scarce in Sussex
'Look-alike' plants: Cranberry is quite distinct in this habitat

Cranberry is a low, evergreen miniature shrub, usually found growing with or creeping over sphagnum mosses. The thread-like stems are prostrate, rooting at intervals, and grow widely spreading and separated. The small 4 to 8mm oblong, pointed leaves are widely separated from each other. They are deep green above and whitish below, with smooth, deeply inrolled margins. The flowers are deep pink, 6 to 10mm on a long stalk, sometimes paired, and with four narrow curled back petals and a conspicuous yellow tuft of stamens below. The roundish berry, 6 to 8mm wide is red when ripe, or brownish and sometimes speckled (resembling tiny birds' eggs in a nest).

In Sussex, Cranberry has been very rare since the loss of many of the boggy areas in which it flourished. It is extinct in East Sussex where it was last seen in boggy ground at Guestling in 1875 – according to the Sussex botanist, Wolley-Dod it was "*extinct soon after that through drainage*". In West Sussex we have three recent sites: Welch's Common, in a bog where it is abundant in a small area, and Hurston Warren where it appeared in the bog 'in sheets' in 1996 after clearance, and a single plant at Newpiece Moor. Hurston Warren is currently managed under an English Nature Wildlife Enhancement Scheme.

Cranberry

The first record from Amberley Wildbrooks was in 1801, but it is sadly no longer found there. In the 1970s local villagers could remember when berries, collected from the Brooks, where they were said to be abundant, were sold in the village – from one shilling to two shillings and sixpence a quart. There were records too from Pulborough, West Chiltington and Greatham early last century.

The berries are rich in vitamin C and are used to produce the fruit juice. Cranberry sauce is the traditional accompaniment to turkey at Christmas, and in the USA at Thanksgiving. Wild collected and commercially farmed berries are imported from many countries around the world for sale in our greengrocers and supermarkets. Cranberries are locally frequent in much of Britain and Ireland, but absent from most of southern England, southern Ireland and the north of Scotland.

In Europe Cranberry grows from Scandinavia to central France, northern Italy, Romania and Poland. Cranberries are also found from northern Asia to Japan and in Greenland, North America and British Columbia.

Dittander (Broad-leaved Pepperwort)
Lepidium latifolium

Cabbage family
Brassicaceae

Habitat: Estuarine creeks and marshes, and on banks of tidal rivers
Height: 50-120cm
Flowering: June and July
Status: Nationally Scarce and Scarce in Sussex
'Look-alike' plants: The broad leaves and very tiny flowers distinguish Dittander from most other members of the cabbage family

Dittander is a perennial with thick branched roots, and it can spread readily from broken small pieces from this rootstock. The long broad, smooth, blue-green leaves grow to 30cm. The basal leaves have long stalks while the upper leaves are stalkless with white margins near the tip. All the margins have distant teeth. The flowers are on branched stems in dense clusters, each flower is very small, approximately 2.5mm across, and their sepals have broad white margins.

Dittander is found growing in saltmarshes and estuarine creeks, as at Fishbourne Creek in West Sussex. It occurs on the banks of tidal rivers as on the River Arun near Burpham, Houghton and Amberley. The occasional inland sites are possibly relics of cultivation, or plants may have grown from fragments of Dittander root stock moved with sand or gravels from coastal areas. All the East Sussex sites are thought to represent introductions made in this way.

Dittander was formally grown and used in a sauce, before pepper and horse radish were available – Gerard in his *Herbal* (1597) describes Dittander as being "*extreme hot*". It was also used in medicine and it is known that Dittander was used at that time as a treatment for leprosy. It is thought that the colony found at Chichester in 1995 might have originated from the gardens of the 12th century leper hospital of St James and Mary Magdelene.

Dittander (Broad-leaved Pepperwort)

Near Burpham, Dittander grows beside the River Arun, near a downland path known as Leper's track. In the past this track led to a leper building.

Dittander is now less widespread in Britain and Europe, but it also grows in North Africa and south west Asia. It was taken in the past by emigrants to North America and Australia, presumably to use as a condiment.

Fly Honeysuckle
Lonicera xylosteum

Honeysuckle family
Caprifoliaceae

Habitat: Open woodland and scrub on chalk
Height: To 2m
Flowering: May
Fruiting: July to September
Status: Red Data Book (Endangered), Scarce in Sussex
'Look-alike' plants: Some garden ornamental honeysuckles

Fly Honeysuckle is a bushy shrub with grey, slightly downy, slender twigs. The leaves are 3 to 6cm long and downy with short hairs, that render it velvety to the touch. The flowers are conspicuously paired with each pair on a single, downy 1 to 2cm long stalk. The yellowish-white tubular flowers (sometimes tinged reddish and downy outside) are about 1cm long. These are pollinated by Bumble-bees (as the flower tube is much shorter than our native hedgerow Wild Honeysuckle and many of the cultivated species). The flowers are followed by paired, round, scarlet-red berries.

In Britain it is only accepted as native in Sussex. In West Sussex it is found on the downland scarp between Amberley and Rackham. This is where the Sussex botanist William Borrer collected a specimen in 1801. In East Sussex there is a single locality at Wilmington in a very similar habitat. At the West Sussex site most of the bushes are within a Special Site of Scientific Interest and a County Wildlife Site, but even here they have been threatened by woodland clearance for game management, by cattle damage and also by clearance for an electricity line – vigilant monitoring is essential for the survival of these rare plants. Over a hundred bushes have been counted at seven localities within the site near Springhead Hill at Amberley Mount.

Fly Honeysuckle

Fly Honeysuckle is a European plant occurring from Scandinavia to Spain, Sicily and the Caucasus, and it grows commonly in mountain woods in the Alps.

Fragrant Orchid

Gymnadenia conopsea

Orchid family
Orchidaceae

Habitat: Chalk grassland
Height: 15-20cm
Flowering: June to July
Status: Not Scarce – but the two subspecies also found in Sussex are Scarce
'Look-alike' plants: Fragrant Orchid subspecies *densiflora* and subspecies *borealis*

The Fragrant Orchid is a typical plant of uncultivated downland turf. This habitat is still common along the whole length of the chalk, but especially so on the East Sussex Downs. Fragrant Orchids also occur occasionally in meadows off the chalk.

From the base are three to five long, narrow, folded and slightly hooded leaves, with another two or three narrow, pointed stem leaves close to the stem above. The flower spike is long and dense with many small flowers, up to 200 on one spike. The tiny flowers are bright pink, with a narrow, green pointed bract below. The side sepals are long and narrow and project downwards and outwards on either side of the lip, with the petals and third sepal forming a loose hood. The shape of the whole flower is characteristically short vertically, but wide from side to side. The lip is short but distinctly three lobed, with a very long slender down-curving spur. This is often translucent showing the nectar in the spur which attracts moths, butterflies and bees. The flowers are strongly scented and it is a memorable day when one finds a downland bank of Fragrant Orchids in full pink flower standing against a summer blue sky.

Fragrant Orchid

In Sussex we have some records of two subspecies of this elegant flower, both of which are scarce plants: *Gymnadenia conopsea* subsp. *densiflora* is restricted to calcareous fens and north facing downland slopes. It is unpredictable in its habits, and often does not appear following a dry spring. It is distinguished by the longer and even denser spike of flowers. It is a robust plant and the flowering spike may be as tall as 75cm! It flowers later than the typical Fragrant Orchid, sometimes into August. We have six records of this subspecies in Sussex – three in West Sussex; at Heyshott Down and at Leythorne Meadow and sparingly in Balcombe Marsh, both Sussex Wildlife Trust nature reserves. In East Sussex the records are from Ditchling Beacon, Blackcap and Beddingham – all downland sites.

The other subspecies *Gymnadenia conopsea* subsp. *borealis* grows in acid pastures, and is mostly northern in its distribution. We have three localities for this subspecies in Sussex, all in East Sussex, at Ashdown Forest, Beddingham and Alciston. This subspecies is a smaller plant with small, dark-pink flowers and a distinctive scent as the flowers smell strongly of cloves. It flowers later in July and August.

Fragrant Orchid is locally common or abundant throughout the British Isles and Ireland, also throughout continental Europe and in north-western Asia.

Gorse (Furze, Whin, Hawth or Hoth)
Ulex europaeus

Pea family
Fabaceae

Habitat: Widespread in grassy places, heathland, and scrub
Height: 60cm-2m
Flowering: March to June, but some plants flower throughout mild winters. Not July to September
Status: Not Scarce
'Look-alike' plants: Dwarf Gorse and Western Gorse

Gorse is a plant that thrives in a damp climate with relatively mild winters. It is has been included in this book as, although it is widespread throughout Britain, it is pleasant to be able to see an interesting wild plant easily and frequently. Gorse is a well-known densely spiny bluish-green shrub with rigid deeply furrowed spines. The flowers are about 1.5cm tall with velvety flower stalks and wide green bracts below the flowers. The bright golden yellow flowers have 'wings' longer than the boat-shaped keel. They are pollinated mainly by Bumble-bees, and the fruit pods (long and narrow like a pea pod but black with grey or brown hairs) are explosive when ripe in summer (quite audibly so on a hot summer's day). The flowers have a strong scent, reminiscent of coconut, and this can be the pervading fragrance in a Gorse-filled area.

Gorse has been called "*one of the landscape plants of Great Britain*" by Grigson (1958), and the profusion of golden blossom on the bushes in spring is definitely a feature of the Sussex landscape. The long flowering season of Gorse prompted the old saying that "*kissing was out of fashion when Gorse was out of bloom*" – it is usually not difficult to find at least one Gorse flower in any month of the year! But Gorse was also an important plant for the rural

Gorse (Furze, Whin, Hawth or Hoth)

economy. The old ovens made of brick in days gone by were often fuelled by gorse faggots. These sticks were cut and bundled at the end of summer, and burnt in the ovens through the winter. Several families would often share one oven. When the sticks were burnt to ashes the ovens were raked clean with long-handled rakes and the Sunday dinners and bread were baked in the residual heat from the bricks. Records of this time are still in place with local names such as *Furze View,* where a field of Gorse used to provide fuel for the ovens of the nearby inn which was the main bakery for the district.

Gorse fuel was also used for local industries such as brick making and lime burning. With the spines crushed, Gorse could also be used to feed farm animals in the winter. Gorse wine is still made in Sussex from the flowers.

Gorse is distributed all over the British Isles and southern Ireland, with the exception of northern Scotland. It is found in most of central Europe, but it is not frost resistant. In the Mediterranean and Greek Islands there are Gorse look-alike plants, but Gorse does not occur there. The golden-flowered bushes seen in these islands are a similar species called *Calycotome.*

Greater Butterfly-orchid

Platanthera chlorantha

Orchid family
Orchidaceae

Habitat: Damp woodlands and grassy places on chalk and Weald clay
Height: 20-40cm
Flowering: Late May to June
Status: Not Scarce
'Look-alike' plants: Lesser Butterfly-orchid

This rather tall, mainly woodland orchid catches the eye with its relatively large, white long-spurred flowers. The two narrowly oval, blunt green leaves are from 5 to 15cm in length and 1 to 5cm wide. They are conspicuous against the leaf litter of an early spring mixed woodland floor. Each spike holds between ten and 25 greenish-white flowers that are heavily fragrant – particularly at night. The well-spaced individual flowers stand out from the stem on short stalks. At each side of each flower there is a long, blunt, wavy-edged spreading petal with the upper petals and sepals forming a broad, loose hood. From the centre of each flower, extending backwards, is a long, curved spur, that can be up to 28mm long. Also in the centre of the flower, the bright yellow pollinia (pollen masses) are conspicuous against the white of the flowers. These are prominent on either side of the entrance to the spur and slope forwards and inwards so that they are closer together at the top. The placing and form of the pollinia is the most reliable way to distinguish the Greater Butterfly-orchid from its (less

Greater Butterfly-orchid

common) 'look-alike' plant the Lesser Butterfly-orchid, in which the pollinia are parallel and do not diverge.

The long, slender spur is not just for show, it holds nectar at its tip ensuring that the flowers are visited by the long-tongued night-flying moths that pollinate this species. The strong sweet scent (which is reminiscent of Freesias) attracts moths and also the greenish-white colour of the flowers has a luminous quality in the evening, so that the Greater Butterfly-orchids stand out distinctly at dusk in a shady woodland.

In Sussex, Greater Butterfly-orchids are scattered across both counties, away from the acid soil forests and heaths and the coastal areas. It does not grow in large colonies, but in small groups, especially in woodlands on base-rich soils at the foot of the Downs, in woodland edges on chalk and in the mixed woodlands on clay in West Sussex near Horsham, Billingshurst, Petworth and Pulborough.

It is found throughout the British Isles and also Europe. Surprisingly, it is a mountainous plant in many places and is found in the Alps, the Caucasus and Siberia.

Hemlock Water-dropwort

Oenanthe crocata

Carrot family
Apiaceae

Habitat: In ditches and by ponds
Height: 50-120cm
Flowering: June and July
Status: Not Scarce
'Look-alike' plants: Other plants of the carrot family, including Wild Celery

Hemlock Water-dropwort is a stout, erect, branched perennial growing from root tubers which are sweet tasting but beware, the whole plant is **very poisonous**. The stems are hollow and grooved, with large leaves of up to 30cm long which are triangular and divided into three or four rounded or oval segments. The stem leaves are narrower and the leaf margins are toothed. The leaf stalks sheath the main stem, and the rayed flower heads are large and rounded, making the plants conspicuous when in flower. The individual flowers are small, a mere 2mm across and with unequal petals in the outer flowers. When in full flower many insects are attracted to the flower heads. The fruits are important in the identification of the plant to distinguish it from other species of Umbellifer.

When in flower Hemlock Water-dropwort is a spectacular feature of the summer countryside, outlining the waterways, massed in shallow water or at pond edges. The danger of the poisonous tubers (they have been mistaken for parsnip) and poisonous, celery-like stems and leaves is always present. A few years ago, some students staying at a youth hostel near Lewes as self-caterers, gathered some Hemlock Water-dropwort for their evening stew, mistaking the plant for Wild Celery. After their meal they collapsed, and were rushed to hospital. Fortunately they all recovered, but the student who had eaten two helpings was in intensive care for some time. Botanically, it is interesting that they were Dutch students, as in Holland Wild Celery is a common waterside Umbellifer, while our common Hemlock Water-dropwort was at that time unknown there. This true story emphasises the caution required when eating wild food and the need for accurate identification.

Hemlock Water-dropwort is also found in France, Spain, Portugal, Italy, Sardinia and Morocco.

Herb-Paris

Paris quadrifolia

Lily family
Liliaceae

Habitat: Damp shady woods on chalky soils
Height: 15-30cm
Flowering: May to July
Status: Scarce in Sussex
'Look-alike' plants:
The curious symmetry of Herb-Paris makes it distinctive

Herb-Paris is a hairless native plant growing from a rhizome with a stem that typically has a single whorl of four (but sometimes five or even six) broadly oval leaves with a short pointed tip. The leaves are between 6 and 12cm long with three to five main veins. The single flower above the leaves on a short stalk is yellow-green, starry, and has lance-shaped, pointed sepals below the thread-like petals. The long-stalked stamens have narrow, greenish anthers, and in the centre a shining berry-like capsule, turning black when it ripens in June and eventually splitting to show red shiny seeds.

In West Sussex the majority of sites for this plant are in the Harting area, at West and South Harting and Tower Hill. In East Sussex just one site exists in Maplehurst Wood near Hastings. At some of these sites there are large patches of 100 plants or more.

Herb-Paris is an ancient woodland incicator and often grows in ancient woodland. There are scattered records for Herb-Paris in Britain, Ireland and the Isle of Man, and it grows in Europe from Iceland, northern Russia, Siberia and the Caucasus to central Spain, Italy, Macedonia and Corsica.

Hoary Cinquefoil
Potentilla argentea

Rose family
Rosaceae

Habitat: Generally confined to open areas on light sandy soils
Height: 15-30cm
Flowering: May to September
Status: Scarce in Sussex
'Look-alike' plants: Trailing Tormentil; distinguished from Creeping Cinquefoil by the leaves, and from Tormentil by the habitat

It is the leaves that are distinctive in this Hoary Cinquefoil. They are deep green above, cut into five narrow, lobed or toothed segments – but turn them over and the undersides are silver with silvery-white felted hairs.

The whole plant is slender and downy, branched and with numerous terminal pale gold, five-petalled flowers 10 to 12mm across. The small clustered fruits are pale yellow.

In Sussex the Hoary Cinquefoil is much less common than it was 50 years ago, and is now extinct in East Sussex. In West Sussex we have eight recent sites, some from sandy commons at West Heath and Coates. Also at Wiggonholt, Rackham and the Pulborough Brooks Royal Society for the Protection of Birds nature reserve.

In Britain it is generally decreasing and now common only in eastern England. In Europe it is found from Scandinavia (where it is a common pavement weed in Oslo), to central Spain, central Italy and Greece. Also Hoary Cinquefoil is found in Asia Minor, Turkestan, and in North America from Nova Scotia to Columbia and Kansas.

Hoary Stock
Matthiola incana

Cabbage family
Brassicaceae

Habitat: On sea cliffs
Height: To 60cm
Flowering: May to August (but one year recorded in flower on a sheltered cliff at Black Rock, Brighton on New Year's Day!)
Status: Nationally scarce
'Look-alike' plants: Sea Stock

Hoary Stock is an annual or shrubby perennial plant, with dense white downy hairs giving it a whitish appearance. The tap root and the stems are stout, and the stems are woody and leafless below. The downy upper leaves are narrow and lance-shaped, and the four-petalled flowers are 2.5 to 5cm across in a loose head, with purple or sometimes white petals.

The narrow seed-pods are held upright on stalks, they are only 3 to 4mm wide but can be from 4 to 13cm long. They are characterised by two small 'horns' at the top. The fragrant flowers are popular with butterflies.

The first British record for this rare plant is from 1806 in Hastings, where it can still be found near the Castle, although it is probably not precisely the same site. It was also known before 1900 near Brighton,

Hoary Stock

and at Rottingdean, Saltdean and Beachy Head. The Sussex botanist Arnold recorded the Hoary Stock on 22 March 1870 as "*under chalk cliffs beyond Kemp Town Brighton*", near what is now the Brighton Marina. The plant is still plentiful there today. Some plants can also be found on the nearby walls of Roedean School.

While the Marina was under construction (in the late 1970s), lengths of cliff were blasted away and cleared of vegetation. Hoary Stock was one of the first colonisers of the newly bared chalk. At the time a few of the plants were white-flowered and for a number of years afterwards the majority of the plants in the area were white-flowered. Recently the population is again purple-flowered.

The Hoary Stock is rare in western Europe but grows in southern Europe, the Canary Islands, North Africa and Asia Minor. In Britain it is considered to be only doubtfully native; it is rare but found in a few localities in north Devon, Glamorgan and the Channel Islands.

Juniper
Juniperus communis

Juniper family
Cupressaceae

Habitat: Downland
Height: To 6m
Flowering: June to July
Status: Scarce in Sussex
'Look-alike' plants:
Juniper is distinctive

Juniper is a bushy shrub with greyish leaves and reddish-brown bark that peels in strips as it ages. The leaves are in whorls of three, 5 to 19mm long, very narrow and with no leaf stalk but jointed at the base and with a spiny point at the tip; they feel prickly to the touch. Each leaf is concave with a broad white band above, and green and keeled below. The male and female flowers are on separate bushes. The solitary male cones are about 8mm, cylindrical and with five or six whorls of scales; the female cones are only about 2mm in size. The blue-black berry-like fruit is rather longer (about 5mm) than broad and it takes two or three years to ripen. They have the powdery appearance of a dusty bloom that you would expect to see on plums and grapes. The ripe fruits are well known for giving the original gin its characteristic flavour. Oil of Juniper was used in digestive mixtures until the first half of the last century, and Juniper wood was burnt in open hearths for its fragrance.

In Sussex Juniper has been a plant of the West Sussex downland, which is more wooded than the bare open ridge of East Sussex. The first Sussex record came from near Mount Caburn in 1792, but more recent *Floras* have all commented on the rarity of Juniper in East Sussex. Fourteen recent records in West Sussex are mostly from the Downs, at the south of the

Juniper

Trundle, Goodwood, Sussex Wildlife Trust's Levin Down nature reserve and from Amberley Mount to Rackham Banks. It is also found at Devil's Dyke, Steyning Round Hill, Worthing Golf Course and Chantry Lane, Storrington.

Juniper is common in Scotland and scattered in Britain and western Ireland. Elsewhere it grows in Arctic and north temperate zones, south to the mountains of the Himalayas; north California and Pennsylvania.

Knapweed Broomrape
Orobanche elatior

Broomrape family
Orobanchaceae

Habitat: Chalk downland, where Greater Knapweed grows
Height: 15-70cm
Flowering: June and July
Status: Scarce in Sussex
'Look-alike' plants: Other broomrapes, Bird's-nest Orchid

Knapweed Broomrape, like other broomrapes, is a root parasite with underground tubers attached to the roots of the host plant. The Broomrape has no leaves or green chlorophyll, but a tall, scaly yellowish or reddish flowering shoot growing above ground. The stem has numerous flowers forming a dense spike. It is a magnificent plant with each flower tinged with pale yellow and a dull purple. Each flower is 18 to 25mm long, and curved with glandular hairs. The upper lip is two-lobed and spreading, the lower three-lobed, with all the lobes crisped and toothed. The rounded yellow stigmas are conspicuous in the open flower.

In Sussex Knapweed Broomrape has always been rare. It grows with its host plant, the Greater Knapweed on dry, chalky grassland. The Broomrape is very much less common there than the host, which is abundant on the Sussex Downs. The Greater Knapweed seems unaffected by the Knapweed Broomrape clinging to its roots and the two plants live together side by side.

Knapweed Broomrape

There are only a few sites in East Sussex for this unusual and fascinating plant. These include Glyndebourne, Hollingbury and Queen's Park Brighton. Likewise in West Sussex it has a limited distribution including The Burgh near Amberley Mount and the chalk-pit at Lavant.

Knapweed Broomrape is occasional but widely distributed throughout England and Wales; in Europe to Denmark and southern Sweden, the Caucasus, Asia Minor and India.

Large-leaved Lime (Linden Tree)

Tilia platyphyllos

Lime family
Tiliaceae

Habitat: Native in Sussex on steep downland scarp. Elsewhere often planted
Height: : To 30m
Flowering: Late June
Status: Nationally Scarce and Scarce in Sussex
'Look-alike' plants: Common Lime and Small-leaved Lime

The Large-leaved Lime is a large tree, up to 30m tall. It has spreading branches and dark grey, finely ribbed bark. The young twigs are velvety with soft short hairs, and the 6 to 12cm leaves are broadly ovate, abruptly pointed at the tip, and obliquely heart-shaped at the base. The leaves are a dark, dull green and almost hairless on the upper surface, pale green and shortly hairy all over the lower surface. There are also whitish tufts of hairs in the angles of its veins. The edge of the leaf is sharp-toothed and its stalk is 1.5 to 5cm in length. The pendulous yellowish-white flowers grow in threes, with stamens longer than the petals. This Lime produces three to five rounded fruits which are densely hairy, 8 to 10mm in circumference, strongly ribbed and woody when mature. The flowers produce a lovely scent but you should avoid parking your car underneath this tree at flowering time as when the sticky nectar drops it will harden!

Large-leaved Lime (Linden Tree)

Until recently it was thought that all the Sussex records for this handsome tree, which is native in central and western Europe, were of planted trees only. There was the possible exception of one very old tree on the northern slope of Chanctonbury Hill, which Borrer (1800-1855) knew as "*one huge old tree*" and this could still be seen there in 1986. In the late 1980s however, trees found on very steep north-facing downland scarp in West Sussex were thought to be possibly native, and this was confirmed by a Lime tree specialist.

Since 1986 the newly determined records for native trees in Sussex have been gathered together. Most are within ancient copses surrounded by woodlands towards the foot of the scarp. At one site at Treyford near Midhurst, the trees are within an ancient downland rew on an old farm boundary, and these are the only records not on the scarp slope. In West Sussex we have 19 other localities at which these trees can be seen, including at Harting, Didling Hanger, Sutton, Barlavington, Springhead Hill and Wolstonbury Hill. There are no records from East Sussex.

'Linden' is the German name for Lime, all species of Lime are referred to as 'Linden Trees'.

Lily-of-the-valley

Convallaria majalis

Lily family
Liliaceae

Habitat: Dry woods
Height: To 20cm
Flowering: May and June
Status: Not scarce
'Look-alike' plants: Well known as a garden plant

The pretty and delicate flowers of Lily-of-the-valley are white-petalled, stalked, nodding and rounded bell-shaped. The two to three stalked, clear green leaves are 8 to 20cm long and anything between 3 and 5cm wide. There may be from six to 12 flowers on each plant – they are strongly sweet scented, and followed later in the year by scarlet berries.

Being such an attractive and sweet-smelling plant it is often cultivated in gardens from where it frequently escapes and naturalises. It is not easy to decide if plants are genuinely wild, but garden escapes are often stouter and more robust than wild plants, which have fewer flowers than those in gardens. In Sussex fewer of the wild plants set ripe fruits. However, whether native or introduced, Lily-of-the-valley is always a delight to find growing in a wild place.

In Sussex we have occasional recent records, and older reports of localities including at Uppark, and Ardingly Rocks, "*plentifully in a dry barren wood in Catsfield Parish*" (first recorded in 1787); also in Dallington, Worth, Tilgate and Wych Cross Forests – and on the top of Harrison's Rocks "*plentifully in 1903*". But the most well known Sussex locality is St. Leonard's Forest, where the Lily-of-the-valley can be still seen today, possibly the only

Lily-of-the-valley

wild flower to be on an Ordnance Survey map, marked as 'Lily Beds' in the Forest. In 1868 G.B. Holmes reported *"large beds well established"* there, but legend associates the lilies with the Forest very much earlier. In 1614 a pamphlet on the legend of the *"Dragon of St. Leonard's Forest – True and wonderful"* was published in London. This is described by Dorothea Hurst in *History and Antiquities of Horsham* (1889), and refers to *"a dragon, winged serpent or a mighty worm in this foreste"* which was killed by St. Leonard, *"the strife was ofttimes renewed in different places and that wheresoever the saint's blood fell to the ground there lilies-of-the-valley sprung up."* And this story is told in an old verse:

"Folks say that in the dreadful fight
He poured his blood, but at the sight
Sweet lilies sprung from out the stain,
Which since have bloomed and bloomed again."

In the 1960s St. Leonard's Lily-of-the-valley was mostly found in the semi-circular fringe of shade from the largest beech trees. When the Forestry Commission felled and replanted the majority of the forest with larch, the Lily Beds area was planted with beech saplings and for many years Horsham Natural History Society members cleared the bracken around these young beech trees enabling this ancient colony of Lily-of-the-valley to survive today.

Lily-of-the-valley grows in scattered localities in Britain, in a number of different habitats. These are mainly chalky, dry woodlands in the south, even though they are seldom found on chalk in Sussex. It is also found in hedgebanks and scrub. In northern England the plants sometimes appear in the 'grykes' of limestone pavements. Across Europe it is often found in alpine woods and scrub.

Little-Robin
Geranium purpureum

Crane's-bill family
Geraniaceae

Habitat: In Sussex it is coastal, in warm open areas on the landward edge of shingle or sand
Height: Prostrate, to 10-20cm
Flowering: May to September
Status: Red Data Book, Lower Risk, Scarce in Sussex
'Look-alike' plants: The small seaside form of Herb Robert

Little-Robin is a small, low-growing coastal plant that is very rare in Sussex. The leaves are palmate (hand-shaped) deeply cut into three broadly toothed segments. The flowers are small with five pink petals and in the centre the stamens have yellow pollen. It is a plant of the Mediterranean, common in south western Europe and Madeira, and eastwards to Turkey and Iran. In Sussex it has been confused with the larger and widespread Herb-Robert, *Geranium robertianum*, particularly with the maritime form which also grows on our coastal sands and shingles. This seaside Herb-Robert is smaller than the common inland form, but distinguished from Little-Robin by its leaf, its strong, rather unpleasant smell, and by its larger flowers with petals 14 to 18mm across. These also have orange pollen on the anthers of the stamens. The beak of the fruiting capsule (which gives the family its English name of crane's-bill) is also longer than that of Little-Robin.

In contrast, Little-Robin has a pleasant aromatic scent, smaller flowers with petals usually not much more than 7mm long, but always less than 14mm, with yellow pollen and the smaller beak to the capsule.

In Sussex our earliest record for Little-Robin was by the botanist John Ray in 1724, when he found it on 'Selsey Island'. Since 1834 there have been

Little-Robin

scattered records in the Middleton-Climping area. For many years until 1975, plants could be found on the edge of the dunes at Climping, but that site was destroyed by a parking development. Little-Robin was not refound in spite of repeated searches there, and it was thought then to be extinct in West Sussex. There was great excitement in 1999 when a new site was found on a beach near Elmer, colonising recent sea defences.

In East Sussex in 2001 Little-Robin was spotted in an unexpected habitat on Lewes railway station, growing profusely on ballast between the railway lines of the London platforms! The staff told us that the plants had been there for some years, but were sprayed with herbicide each year, presumably after the seed had set, and the Little-Robin reappeared for a brief flowering the following year. It is likely that the plants are also on Polegate station, but of course if a possible specimen is seen the railway staff must be asked for assistance to collect one to confirm that it has yellow anthers.

Since 1982 there have been fewer British records, and in Sussex, although there have been intermittent sightings for nearly 280 years, these are few and the present colonies are very vulnerable to movement by the shingle and the coastal plants could quickly disappear again.

Marsh Cinquefoil
Potentilla palustris

Rose family
Rosaceae

Habitat: Marshes and bogs on peaty soil
Height: 15-35cm
Flowering: May to July
Status: Scarce in Sussex
'Look-alike' plants: Water Avens – but this differs in flowers, leaf and habitat

Marsh Cinquefoil is a distinguished plant, eye-catching with its unusual colouring for a wild flower. The lower leaves have long stalks and five to seven pinnate leaflets 3 to 6cm long, oblong and sharply toothed. The flowers, 2 to 3cm across on a branched, glandular hairy stem, are star-shaped with five broad purplish pointed sepals, and five maroon or purple linear petals (thus the name Cinquefoil) that are much shorter than the sepals. The stamens, styles and fruits are also deep purple. The flowers are dependant on insect visitors for pollination.

Common in most of Britain and Ireland, the Marsh Cinquefoil is, however, very localised in southern England. In Sussex the first record was described by Pettiver (1714) as found in 1713 "*in a bog near the road from Pett to Winchelsea*" in East Sussex. Marsh Cinquefoil was still to be found here in the 1930s, but many sites and habitats for this plant have been lost in the last 50

Marsh Cinquefoil

years. Its habitat is threatened by the drainage of marshes and bogs. We now only have seven Sussex localities for this unusual and dramatic flower. Four sites are in East Sussex, including nature reserves at Park Corner Heath by a pond and Hooe Common in a marsh. In West Sussex there are four localities, with two sites at Amberley Wildbrooks nature reserve in damp grassland by ditches; one in an acid bog at Welchs Common on Burton Pond Local Nature Reserve; one at Lindfield in damp grassland and one at West Chiltington.

In Europe the Marsh Cinquefoil grows from Iceland and arctic Russia to mountain areas in central Spain, northern Italy, Bulgaria and the Caucasus; it also occurs in temperate Asia to Armenia, Turkestan and Japan, as well as northern America and Greenland.

Meadow Clary

Salvia pratensis

Dead-nettle family
Lamiaceae

Habitat: Grassland and scrub on chalk
Height: 30-100cm
Flowering: Late May to early July, and occasional later flowers in September
Status: Red Data Book (Lower Risk), Schedule 8 and Scarce in Sussex
'Look-alike' plants: Wild Clary – but the flowers of this are smaller and not wide open

Meadow Clary is an aromatic perennial. It has two or three pairs of stalkless softly hairy and glandular leaves above. The lower leaves are stalked, 7 to 15cm long, oval, blunt and heart-shaped at the base. They are wrinkled and with wavy edges. The deep sky-blue or violet-blue flowers are in whorls of four to six up the stem. They are open with the upper lip glandular and strongly curved, forming a hood. Some flowers of Meadow Clary are hermaphrodite, carrying both male and female organs, others which are female only are much smaller. The bracts under the flowers are green and about half the length of the sepals. The flowers are pollinated by long-tongued Bumble-bees.

Meadow Clary has always been rare in Sussex, with only occasional records documented since 1887 – however some of these were casual introductions and the plants did not persist.

Meadow Clary

During the time of the survey for the *Sussex Plant Atlas* (1966-1980), the only locality known for Meadow Clary, was on a downland slope at Lancing. These plants dwindled away and it was thought that Meadow Clary was extinct in Sussex. However, since 1986 it has been found in three localities in West Sussex, two of them at and above Anchor Bottom, Upper Beeding, where there is a good colony, although it has been severely grazed in some years. It is hoped that negotiations with the farmer can lessen this. In 1998 a new site was found in a field in the grounds of Roedean School, and this is the only recent East Sussex record.

In Britain Meadow Clary has been rare and occasional, but only in England where it was grown here in Elizabethan gardens for ornamental purposes. In Europe it is found from Scandinavia to the Pyrenees, through central Italy, Slovenia, Serbia and Bulgaria to Turkey and the Urals. Meadow Clary is common just across the Channel, and is often the first 'new' plant to catch the eye along the roadsides in France. It is also common on Swiss roadsides and railway banks.

Medlar
Mespilus germanica

Rose family
Rosaceae

Habitat: Naturalised in hedges
Height: 2-3m
Flowering: May and June
Status: Scarce in Sussex
'Look-alike' plants: The large flowers of Medlar distinguish it from the other white-flowered shrubs of this family

Medlar is a thorny shrub growing to 2 or 3m in hedgerows. However, when grown as a tree with space around, it is thornless and grows up to 6m. The young twigs are densely hairy, but smooth, blackish and stiff when older. The leaves are spear-shaped, 5 to 12cm long, usually with a few teeth on the margins towards the pointed tip, and shiny on top with some close hairs on the underside. The flowers grow on a short downy stalk, with leafy sepals below, often longer than the 12mm rounded wavy-edged petals. Medlar flowers are mostly white, but occasionally very pale pink. These beautiful large, open, cup-shaped flowers, nearly 4cm across, are solitary on short leafy shoots. The rounded brown fruits crowned by the persistent sepals are only edible when they are almost rotten.

Most of the Medlar sites in Sussex are of older trees originally from gardens or orchards, but some are long-established in old hedgerows. Near Battle in East Sussex there is a record from the Sussex botanist Borrer in 1839. Arnold in his 1887 *Flora* mentions old trees in hedgerows near Battle,

Medlar

Guestling and Hastings. These trees remain today. In West Sussex there is a fine example to be found at the southern end of Burton Mill car park, near Fittleworth.

Medlar trees can be grown in gardens where, with some space, its branches will droop, making a sheltered playhouse for children. In autumn the leaves turn a deep glowing red. Since ancient times Medlars have been known for their medicinal qualities, and were given for diarrhoea and eaten by women to prevent haemorrhages. Early in the 20th century a chemical analysis showed that Medlars contained pectins, tannins and sugars, and the fruit was declared to be *"the perfect regulator of the stomach"*. Although the fruit is now too rare to pick in the wild, garden grown Medlars can be picked as they soften and used to produce a delicious sharp jelly, which is particularly good served with meat and cheese.

Old records show that Medlars have been naturalised in hedges for at least four centuries in southern England. Medlar is native to south eastern Europe, Turkey and south western Asia.

Mousetail
Myosurus minimus

Buttercup family
Ranunculaceae

Habitat: Damp bare fields
Height: 5-10cm
Flowering: June and July
Status: In Sussex it is scarce and sporadic in appearance. It is declining in West Sussex and has disappeared from East Sussex
'Look-alike' plants: Fruiting spikes resemble a small plantain

Mousetail is an intriguing but inconspicuous small, hairless annual. In Sussex is found mainly in fields trampled by cattle. The leaves grow up from a basal rosette and they are narrow, smooth and somewhat fleshy. The many erect flowering stems each have one flower with five pale, greenish-yellow petals at the tip. Even as the flowers first open, the fruiting spike can be seen growing from the centre. It elongates as it ripens and can be as long as 7cm, giving the little plant its Mousetail name.

Bare, open, damp soil is essential for Mousetail germination, and the plants are quite often found in field gateways where cattle have crowded through and trampled the ground. Most of our West Sussex records are from sites that have been very much influenced by cattle or farm vehicles. As areas are colonised by more aggressive weeds, Mousetail is often crowded out, but long-lived seeds in the soil enable the plant to re-appear when conditions are right again. Two of the recent records are from winter-wet hollows in pastures. We would always be pleased to hear of sightings of this unpredictable plant.

Mousetail

Mousetail is found at scattered localities throughout lowland England from Northumberland to Devon, Kent to north Wales and the Channel Islands. Beyond Britain it is found in central and southern Europe, north Africa and south western Asia. It has also been introduced into North America and Australia, where in some places it has become naturalised.

Narrow-leaved Water-dropwort
Oenanthe silaifolia

Carrot family
Apiaceae

Habitat: Marshy fields and ditches
Height: 30-70cm
Flowering: May to early June
Status: Nationally Scarce
'Look-alike' plants: Other plants of the carrot family growing in damp places

Narrow-leaved Water-dropwort is Nationally Scarce and mostly restricted to a few sites in southern England, but in West Sussex the Arun Valley is a stronghold for this plant, particularly along the river banks and in adjoining unimproved pasture fields.

Narrow-leaved Water-dropwort is an erect perennial with hollow and grooved stems. The leaves are divided into two to four linear segments. The branching rays of the flower head, with each branch topped by the small white flowers 3-4mm across, and the petals of the outer flowers unequal in size are characteristic of and similar to other members of the carrot family. The umbel rays thicken in fruit, and the shape and measurements of these fruits are vital diagnostic tools for precise identification; a *Flora* or the handbook, *Umbellifers of the British Isles* should be consulted. A good hint for the identification of Narrow-leaved Water-dropwort is the early flowering time, earlier than most of its 'look-alike' plants, combined with the habitat.

Some of the West Sussex records have been of large populations, as in fields at Watersfield and near Stopham Bridge, where in good flowering years the fields or field edges can be white with the Narrow-leaved Water-dropwort at the end of May. However, in some sites the plants are more cryptic as they are restricted to the river or ditch bank, or may be only one plant in each riverside field.

Narrow-leaved Water-dropwort

The Narrow-leaved Water-dropwort is quickly eliminated by quite modest agricultural intensification. It has been reported that 'improvement' is its downfall. Conversely where the water meadows have been positively managed to restore damp meadow grassland, as at the Royal Society for the Protection of Birds Pulborough Brooks Nature Reserve where the hay meadow regime has been re-instated the Narrow-leaved Water-dropwort has moved back from the ditches and recolonised some fields.

Unlike other members of the carrot family, Narrow-leaved Water-dropwort is not known for aromatic plant chemicals. These are well known and in common use in Fennel, Caraway, Carrot, Coriander, Dill, Chervil, Lovage and Parsley. But beware, as other members of the same family are some of our most notorious poisonous plants including Hemlock, Hemlock Water-dropwort, Cowbane and Giant Hogweed, which can cause dermatitis in contact with skin in sunlight. There is also Fool's Parsley, that has a similar leaf structure to Parsley. This underlines the importance of correct identification.

This Umbellifer grows in parts of France, Portugal, Italy and south eastern Europe, where the agriculture is less intensive; also in south west Asia and north Africa.

Pheasant's-eye

Adonis annua

Buttercup family
Ranunculaceae

Habitat: Formerly a plant of cultivated fields on chalk, now mainly restricted to disturbed ground and waste places
Height: 7-20cm
Flowering: early June to July
Status: Red Data Book Species (Vulnerable), and Scarce in Sussex
'Look-alike' plants: None

Pheasant's-eye was at one time so plentiful in South East England that bunches were picked and sold in Covent Garden Market. How this species came to Britain is unclear. Botanists differ in their opinions, but it is either native or a very ancient introduction. It is still sometimes grown in gardens. Gerard the Herbalist knew this flower as 'Rose-a-ruby', and wrote that he grew it in his 16th century garden.

The flowers are 1.5 to 2.5cm across with bright scarlet petals that have a black spot at the base. Characteristic oval green fruiting heads elongate as the single fruits ripen.

There has been a dramatic decline in numbers for this species, possibly due partly to climatic changes, as it is a Mediterranean plant unable to set seed in cool wet summers. A significant factor in its decline is the more efficient cleaning of crop seed and more intensive agriculture of recent years.

Pheasant's-eye has long been extinct in West Sussex, but in East Sussex, apart from very occasional casual records, it does have a persistent stronghold in Friston Forest, where it can be seen in different newly disturbed areas in most years. These will be areas cleared for tree planting or

Pheasant's-eye

in forest rides following rotovation. In most years there may be a few plants, but only twice (in 1978 and 1996), the plants have appeared in thousands, each time in a different locality – a wonderful sight, but they have not been seen since at either place again.

The seeds are heavy and do not disperse readily to colonise new areas, but they are very long-lived in the soil, giving the hope of future displays to be seen in years ahead.

This charming wild flower has been steadily declining in Sussex since the 1880s, and it is now almost extinct – as it is in the rest of England. It is not threatened in Europe and it also grows eastwards to Iran and southwards to northern Africa.

Field Poppies

Papaver rhoeas and other species

Poppy family
Papaveraceae

Habitat: Weeds of arable fields or field margins, setaside and disturbed chalk on tracks and roadsides
Height: Up to 50cm
Flowering: June to July
Status: Some decreasing
'Look-alike' plants: The different species of Field Poppies are generally distinguished from each other by seed capsule, and shade of red petals

The seed capsules of poppies form early and it is often possible to use these for identification before the flower petals fall, thus each of the poppy species found in Sussex are distinctive. Prickly Poppy *Papaver argemone* is distinguished by the paler, orange-scarlet petals and the narrow capsule with sparse bristly hairs. Common Poppy *Papaver rhoeas* has bright scarlet petals and smooth, oval flat-topped capsules. Rough Poppy is distinguished by powder-blue anthers, deep crimson petals and capsules that are roundish and densely covered with stiff, yellowish bristles. All these can be found at the edges of our arable fields.

Cornfield Poppies were almost certainly introduced as an agricultural weed in ancient times. No-one can truly say where poppies originated (they were recorded in Ancient Egypt c2,500 B.C.), but as agriculture developed around the world, Poppies followed.

The Rough Poppy is an annual with a slender root and branched stiffly hairy stems. The rubbery latex from these stems is white. The leaves are branched two to three times with a bristle point at the tip. The flowers are 2 to 5cm across, have over-lapping petals with bristly sepals below. The soft, papery, roundish, crimson petals have a blackish blotch at the base. The anthers are powder blue and the disk at the top of the capsule has four to eight rays.

The Common Poppy has a very efficient seed dispersal method (17,000

Field Poppies

seeds per plant!), but for all poppies open-ground is essential for germination. The seeds are very long-lived in the soil (over 200 years) and areas of new ploughing or disturbance may be followed by spectacular displays of thousands of scarlet poppies, as on the South Downs in some recent years.

Modern seed cleaning and the widespread use of herbicides and fertilisers has led to a dramatic decrease in the abundance of all poppy species. In Sussex most sites for the Rough Poppy are from the margins of crops where the chemical sprays have not been so intense, or from field edges and tracksides on chalky, well-drained or disturbed soils. They have been found on the Trundle and Cissbury Ring near arable fields; in East Sussex from setaside at Jevington and Southwick Hill, and from arable land at Beachy Head.

Field Poppies are considered to be threatened with extinction or vulnerable in most of the countries of north-west Europe, but also grow in the lowlands of central and southern Europe and eastwards to North Africa and India. Common Poppy has been introduced in North America, Australia and New Zealand.

Sand Catchfly (Striated Catchfly)

Silene conica

Pink family
Caryophyllaceae

Habitat: Chalky sand, often by sea
Height: 10-30cm
Flowering: May to August
Status: Nationally Scarce and Scarce in Sussex
'Look-alike' plants: The wide flask-shaped calyx and small flowers distinguish this from other catchflies

The Sand Catchfly is a sticky, densely hairy, leaning or erect annual that grows up to 30cm high. The greyish, linear, sharp-pointed leaves are paired and opposite up the stem. The lower leaves are stalked and the upper leaves unstalked. Its few, small, rose-pink to almost white flowers are around 5mm across. The ring of sepals, or calyx, is fused forming a distinctive 'flask' that is oval, conical and strongly ribbed. This 'flask' becomes greatly inflated in fruit with six slender teeth at the top.

In Sussex Sand Catchfly is restricted to dunes and path edges at Climping, West Sussex, where it has been recorded since 1885. It is seen in at least four sites in Climping, though the number of flowering plants fluctuates considerably from year to year. In some years it is found in large numbers, but it is dependant on hot summers for good seed production. Since the hot summers of 1989 and 1990 the number of plants at Climping has increased considerably, and they have now spread along the dunes behind the shingle.

In Britain, Sand Catchfly occurs mainly in the Breckland, Norfolk and West Sussex. Other populations are scattered, small and vulnerable so the large population and spreading colony at Climping is of national significance and

Sand Catchfly (Striated Catchfly)

importance. Elsewhere in Britain, Sand Catchfly has maintained its population in Breckland, although it is declining in other parts of East Anglia. In Kent the species is just holding its own in two localities, and survives still at an inland locality on a sandy common in Worcestershire, but only just. There are also records from the Channel Islands.

Sand Catchfly flourishes in south western and central Europe. It is abundant through most of the Mediterranean region, but is absent from some of the Islands. It is also found in north Africa and south west Asia.

Sea Pea
Lathyrus japonicus

Pea family
Fabaceae

Habitat: Shingle beaches
Height: Creeping and ascending
to 30-90cm
Flowering: June to August
Status: Nationally Scarce and
Scarce in Sussex
'Look-alike' plants: Marsh Pea
and Bitter Vetch – but differs in
leaves and habitats

Sea Pea is a blue-green hairless perennial with special adaptations enabling it to grow and flourish in the harsh environment of loose shingle. The deep roots give the plant access to fresh water from below the shingle, supplemented by condensation between the pebbles, and rain. The plants are low-lying and sprawling on the beach, but have upright flower stems. The three or four pairs of broadly oval leaflets are 2 to 4cm long, with the leaf stalk ending in a simple or branched tendril. The five to 15 striking purple-bluish flowers, often with a paler keel, are on a stalk shorter than the leaves. The flowers are pollinated by Bumble-bees.

The 3 to 5cm pods contain up to eight peas, which may float away and disperse to establish a plant on a new beach, as occurred at Church Norton in West Sussex in the 1960s, when a single plant flowered, but did not persist to form a new colony. In earlier centuries humans ate the peas and where the Sea Pea was abundant on the extensive shingles of the Suffolk coast, the peas were said to have sustained the local inhabitants in times of famine.

In Britain the Sea Pea is found mainly on the south eastern coast of England and it is still plentiful on Suffolk shingles and on Chesil Beach in Dorset. Further north and west in Britain it has declined, and can be found

Sea Pea

now in only a few scattered sites. The Sea Pea is threatened by trampling where the beaches are popular and heavily used by the public.

In Sussex the Sea Pea has always been rare, and established only in East Sussex where it has long been known at Winchelsea and Rye. It was first recorded there in 1640 by J. Parkinson as: "*Suffolke Sea Pease at Rie and Pensie in Sussex*". Good colonies are still present, some within the Rye Harbour Local Nature Reserve.

The wider distribution of the Sea Pea is from southern England and Denmark to the Arctic where it is circumpolar, growing on the coasts of northern Russia, Siberia, Kamchatka, China and North America. The Sea Pea of Arctic regions has slightly larger flowers and is a different sub-species from those of our Sussex shingle.

Sea Rocket
Cakile maritima

Cabbage family
Brassicaceae (Cruciferae)

Habitat: A coastal plant tolerant of sea spray
Height: 15-40cm
Flowering: June to August
Status: Scarce in Sussex
'Look-alike' plants: Distinguished from other four-petalled, pink coastal flowers such as Sea Stock and Scurvy Grass as flowers are small and pale

Sea Rocket is a driftline plant usually growing on sand near the edge of the waves, or on the dunes and occasionally on gravel or shingle.

It is a smooth, greyish annual with a very long slender tap-root, which can reach water deep below the dry sand on which the plant is growing. It can be quite tall and branched, but in Sussex it is usually almost prostrate. The leaves are succulent and most often lobed, but as with Salad Rocket, some are linear. The pale lilac or white flowers have four petals, each flower is 6 to 12mm across; the fruits are 10 to 20mm long, in two sections. The upper section is oval and the lower has two projections at the side. When ripe they are buoyant and are dispersed by the tides to colonise new areas of beach. A high concentration of salt can inhibit germination of the seeds, but the salt is washed out by rain. Seeds floated along the shore find very favourable conditions for germination in the nutrient-rich driftlines on sand after high spring tides, especially in rainy weather. Then their rapid germination and growth can exploit their unstable habitat.

The Latin name *Cakile,* is from the Arabic 'Kalali' for Saltwort. It is one of the most characteristic plants of the sandy beaches and open dunes around Britain. It is also found less frequently growing on maritime shingle.

Sea Rocket

Sea Rocket has been decreasing over the past 100 years in Sussex, and we now have only three sites in East Sussex at Camber, Seaford and Brighton Marina. In West Sussex it is slightly more abundant with eight records including Lancing, Climping and East Head. Native in Britain, Sea Rocket grows on the Atlantic coasts of Europe, with related subspecies around the Baltic, Mediterranean and Black Sea.

Sea Rocket has been introduced to North and South America and to Australia, probably with ballast in the holds of sailing ships. Native Americans used to grind the tap-roots of Sea Rocket to add to their flour in hard times and it was known to them as a famine plant.

Sheep's-bit

Jasione montana

Bellflower family
Campanulaceae

Habitat: Sandy or grassy banks on acid soils and on walls
Height: 5-30cm
Flowering: May to August
Status: Scarce in Sussex
'Look-alike' plants: Devil's-bit Scabious, but this is a plant of damp marshes, meadows, chalk grassland and woodland glades

Sheep's-bit is a downy, softly hairy, usually biennial, plant with linear-oblong leaves up to 5cm long. The upper half of the stems are leafless, with single blue flower heads from 5 to 35mm across. The flower heads are rounded above, rather resembling small blue powder puffs when in flower, with small triangular green bracts below. The individual flowers are 5mm long, in tiny spreading bell-shaped tubes.

Sheep's-bit is scattered through the British Isles, occasionally abundant but colonies can consist of just one or two plants. The plant is comparatively abundant in West Sussex, mostly on the sandy commons at Heyshott, Graffham and Midhurst. For many years there has been a clump among the graves in Coldwaltham Churchyard. In times of drought there has been a notice alongside requesting visitors to water the clump!

In East Sussex we have no recent records, in spite of searches by local botanists at old sites, so we must assume that it is now extinct. In the *Sussex Plant Atlas* (1980) there were six records, although even then it was reported as rare in East Sussex. Many East Sussex sites were lost before the 1930s and others have declined in the last 40 years as coarser vegetation increased. There is always the chance of refinding this plant, and we would be delighted to hear of any sightings.

Sheep's-bit

Sheep's-bit is now rare in central, southern and eastern England. This is due to the loss of lowland heath. It occurs on acidic, shallow, well-drained soils – a habitat scarce in Sussex. Sheep's-bit gained its name from its suitability for grazing and it is a reduction in this activity which has furthered its decline.

Sheep's-bit is found in most European countries.

(See page 3 for note on new sightings of Sheep's-bit in Sussex)

Shepherd's-needle (Puck-needle)

Scandix pecten-veneris

Carrot family
Apiaceae

Habitat: Arable fields and field edges
Height: 10-35cm
Flowering: April to July
Status: Nationally Scarce and Scarce in Sussex
'Look-alike' plants: When in fruit Shepherd's-needle
is unmistakable

Shepherd's-needle is a low-growing, almost hairless annual with fern-like leaves. The flower heads are opposite the leaves, each with a simple umbel of one to three rays of minute white flowers 1 to 2mm across. The white petals are oblong, with those of the outer flowers usually larger. Even when the flowers are freshly open the 'needle' fruits begin to elongate taking the flowers with them at the tops of the 'needle' beaks.

These fruits are almost cylindrical, from 2cm long and finally may be to 8cm long. They give this plant the English name of Shepherd's-needle, and the Latin name meaning '*Venus comb*'. The long, beaked fruits are ridged, and have two short persistent styles at the tip.

The seeds of Shepherd's-needle do not live long in the soil and need suitable conditions for germination soon after they have dropped. Most germinate in the autumn and grow with crops. Plants in the UK grow with crops of winter cereals and may be threatened by pre-sowing cultivation which can destroy the small young seedlings of the Shepherd's-needle. The plants were at one time so abundant that there were reports that it impeded mechanical harvesters, but following the introduction of chemical herbicides there has been a rapid drop the in numbers of plants.

In Sussex Shepherd's-needle has followed the same pattern of loss, but we still have nearly a dozen sites. In West Sussex one sympathetic farmer covered his Shepherd's-needle colony with potato sacks before spraying

Shepherd's-needle (Puck-needle)

when he had the need for some light herbicide on his crop. Most West Sussex records are from arable fields as at Itchenor, West Chiltington, Edburton, West Ashling, Lavant, and Mundham. In East Sussex there are two sites near Roedean on cliff top verges, and one in an arable field at Upper Berwick.

Old Sussex names for this plant include Hedgehogs (as in Dorset and Somerset too) and Puck-needle or Pook-needle (also in Hampshire). When growing in quantity amongst the stalks of the wheat it would have been conspicuous when the long, narrow fruits grew up in a row like a pack of needles or the teeth of a comb.

In Europe it is a Mediterranean plant extending west to Britain and north to Denmark; in Scandinavia it is found only as a casual. It grows in north Africa and south west Asia to the borders of India. It has been introduced with crop seeds into many countries, including North and South America, South Africa, Australia and New Zealand.

Small-flowered Buttercup
Ranunculus parviflorus

Buttercup family
Ranunculaceae

Habitat: Open ground on well-drained soils, often near the sea
Height: 10-15cm
Flowering: May to July
Status: Not Scarce
'Look-alike' plants: Other buttercups with small flowers although they are all very different in the leaves and the fruits

The Small-flowered Buttercup is a yellow-green, hairy, spreading annual, with very petite yellow-petalled flowers. The lower leaves are stalked with three to five toothed lobes; the upper leaves are smaller, simple or have oblong lobes. The small pale yellow flowers are opposite the leaves or in the forks of the branched stem. The five (or sometimes fewer) oblong petals are 1 to 2mm long, and are strongly recurved below the sepals. The few central achene fruits are 2.5 to 3mm, roundish with a short curved beak, a narrowly thickened rim and the flattened reddish-brown sides are covered with small 'warts'.

As an arable weed, Small-flowered Buttercup was once abundant but is now relatively infrequent. In recent years it has been found in a few more Sussex sites. This buttercup was thought to be Nationally Scarce, but more recent records show that this is not the case, and in Sussex it appears to have increased since 1986, with several sites in East and West Sussex – mostly from disturbed ground, open chalky banks, or sandy arable fields.

It has long been known in West Sussex at Kingley Vale National Nature Reserve, where it sometimes grows on the disturbed soil of molehills, and in 2000, thousands of plants were seen on the reserve on rabbit disturbed slopes. It has also been recorded near the Information Centre at Sidlesham. In East Sussex there are records from High and Over, and from cliff top grassland on the Seven Sisters.

Small-flowered Buttercup

There are eight species of yellow buttercup found in Sussex – including one Celandine and two Spearworts, which also have yellow flowers. Additionally, we have a number of species of white-flowered, aquatic Water-crowfoots, which are also in the buttercup family. Apart from the general appearance of the buttercup plants and their habitats, the diagnostic character of each is the shape, colour and surface of their fruits, the Small-flowered Buttercup being quite distinctive.

Of the eight yellow buttercups, Small-flowered Buttercup is the second scarcest, the most threatened being the Corn Buttercup *Ranunculus arvensis*.

Small-flowered Buttercup grows throughout England and Wales, but is absent from Scotland and rare in Ireland. It also grows in the Channel Islands, in south and south west Europe, north Africa and western Asia. It is possible that the increased records of this buttercup from Sussex could be due to the succession of relatively mild winters since 1986.

Spiked Rampion
Phyteuma spicatum

Bellflower family
Campanulaceae

Habitat: Woodland and hedgerows on acid soils
Height: 50-80cm
Flowering: Late May and June
Status: Red Data Book (Vulnerable), Schedule 8 and Scarce in Sussex
'Look-alike' plants: A very distinctive flower

Spiked Rampion is a robust, hairless perennial, with long-stalked, ovate, blunt, lower leaves which are finely toothed and heart-shaped at the base. The upper leaves are smaller and narrow without stalks. The dense flower spike at the top of the stem is greenish-ivory as the flower buds open. As it flowers it elongates to about 8cm, with the lowest flowers browning as they age. Each flower is about 1cm long and is curved and cylindrical in bud, with the lobes later separating to the base. The spike may elongate further to 12cm in fruit.

The only established plants of Spiked Rampion in Britain are those in East Sussex. In 1872 it was reported as growing in hedgerows *"scattered for miles"*; but now there are fewer sites and plants. The plants have been monitored and counted, and in 2000 there were fewer than 500 plants in seven sites in the Heathfield and Hailsham areas. Many are in woodlands, and it is thought that change of management from traditional coppicing has resulted in the loss of many colonies. Spiked Rampion plants are very sensitive to heavy shade, and disappear quickly in woodland that is overgrown, so that management is urgently required for the survival of the remaining colonies.

Spiked Rampion

Some of the current sites in East Sussex are on damp summer-shaded roadside verges, others are on edges of woodland rides as in Abbots Wood.

On the continent this species is a common plant of roadside banks and alpine hay meadows. It is endemic to Europe and grows from southern Norway and the Baltic states southwards to northern Spain, Italy and Romania.

Spiked Star-of-Bethlehem
Ornithogalum pyrenaicum

Lily family
Liliaceae

Habitat: Woods and scrub
Height: 50-90cm
Flowering: June to July
Status: Nationally Scarce and Scarce in Sussex
'Look-alike' plants: The Spiked Star-of-Bethlehem is distinctive

Growing from a bulb, the 30 to 60cm limp blue-green leaves of the Spiked Star-of-Bethlehem appear in spring and wither early. The tall straight flower stem carries more than 20 flowers, each greenish-white, delicate and with a band of deeper green on the backs of the 6 to 10mm long petals.

In West Sussex, the Spiked Star-of-Bethlehem has been known from grassy areas of scrub near Fishbourne Church since 1724, and plants can still be found there. In 1987 some were to be destroyed by road widening, and members of the Sussex Botanical Recording Society transplanted them to the grassy banks of a roadside rew nearby. It is an attractive plant, and thus cultivated in gardens – indeed it is thought that all the other West Sussex records are in fact escapes from gardens. Spiked Star-of-Bethlehem has never been recorded in East Sussex.

This is a plant of south western England and is also known also as Bath Asparagus. It sometimes grows abundantly in Somerset and West Gloucester; bunches were once picked here before the flowers fully opened, and sold in Bristol and Bath. They were eaten as asparagus, and Geoffrey Grigson (1958) describes it as delicious, but adds that any self respecting botanist would only eat it if they had to – on conservation grounds!

Spiked Star-of-Bethlehem also grows in Belgium, south and west Switzerland and Austria to the mountains of Spain and Portugal, Italy and Greece; Asia Minor and the mountains of Morocco.

Starry Clover
Trifolium stellatum

Pea family
Fabaceae

Habitat: Coastal shingle
Height: 10-15cm
Flowering: June to August
Status: Scarce in Sussex
'Look-alike' plants: Other Clovers, but Starry Clover is distinctive in fruit, with persistent starry sepals

The Starry Clover is a low upright perennial clover that is softly hairy. The three trefoil leaflets are stalked, bluntly oval, heart-shaped and about 1cm long with scattered hairs on the margins, toothed edges and notched at the top. The flower-heads, on 12 to 15mm hairy stalks, are roundish or oblong with many narrow, long pea-shaped cream or pale pink flowers on each head. The sepals around each flower are densely white and hairy with long slender teeth, edged with hairs, and as long as the flower. The long lobes of the sepals open and spread in fruit and remain on the flower heads for many weeks as starry reddish sepal lobes.

Starry Clover is recorded in Britain as an occasional casual, but only in West Sussex, as a well-naturalised colony where it has been known for 200 years on shingle at Shoreham. This is noted by Sussex botanist Arnold in his 1907 Sussex Flora *"perfectly naturalized on the ballast along Shoreham Harbour, where it has maintained its position since 1804"*. The origin of Starry Clover in Britain is difficult to prove – but Shoreham Harbour was a busy port in 1804 with cargo ships from around the world docking there. It was suggested that Starry Clover might have come in with ballast from Greece – and was reported as still plentiful at Shoreham in 1884. Through the last century it was threatened by increased building over the harbour shingle, and in 1927 *Country Life* published a letter reporting that although in 1926 it had been found *"halfway between the Redoubt and Norfolk Bridge"* no plants could be

Starry Clover

found in 1927. The writer feared that the Starry Clover might have vanished from the Sussex Flora due to the "*progressive zeal of the citizens of Bungalow Town*". However some seed has ensured plants surviving in odd corners, and so they do to this day – in spite of frequent reports through the years that Starry Clover had disappeared. In the 1960s on a rockery in a semi-wild garden along Riverside Gardens, the Starry Clover grew in profusion, apparently safe for the future – but unfortunately seawater inundated the gardens in heavy storms with exceptionally high tides and the clover did not survive.

Now the Starry Clover has been monitored annually for many years, and each year at least one or two plants are reported in corners of remaining shingle or on the beach.

As it was so scarce, it was added to the first *Red Data Book*, but has been excluded in the latest edition as introduced species are no longer covered.

Starry Clover is really a Sussex plant, although it does occasionally also turn up in Hampshire. It is a common plant of the Mediterranean region where it grows in fields, on roadsides and on stony slopes. It is frequently spotted by holiday-makers with an interest in flowers, in any Mediterranean country.

Thorow-wax (Hare's-ear)

Bupleurum rotundifolium

Carrot family
Apiaceae (Umbelliferae)

Habitat: Formerly an abundant weed in cornfields
Height: 15-20cm
Flowering: June and July – occasional late-flowering in stubble until killed by frosts (before it became extinct).
Status: Extinct as a wild plant in Britain
'Look-alike' plants: False Thorow-wax

This erect blue-green annual, with a hollow stem, has very characteristic rounded leaves approximately 2.5cm in diameter, encircling the stem. These leaves are smooth and waxy in appearance and the English name Thorow-wax comes from their shape with main stems threaded through the leaves. This is reminiscent of cobblers pulling their thread through a hole in their beeswax to give the waxed thread used when cobbling.

Below the flowers are broadly oval bracteoles, and the small yellow flowers develop into rounded slightly ridged fruits 3mm across. Formerly common in Sussex cornfields – Wolley-Dod in his *Flora* records it as "*an abundant weed in corn about Warnham and Rusper*" in 1862. About 100 years later it was extinct throughout Britain – another victim of the more efficient cleaning of grain seed for the crops.

Occasional casual records at first thought to be Thorow-wax were found to be the easily confused False Thorow-wax which has narrower leaves. This Hare's-ear from eastern Europe was imported in bird seed and appeared spontaneously in gardens after feeding the birds.

The Thorow-wax does still grow as an arable weed and in dry grassy places in southern and eastern Europe and in Russia. More recently it has

Thorow-wax (Hare's-ear)

been grown in Holland as a commercial florist's flower, where it is seen in almost every yellow, green or mixed flower bouquet. Some of this Thorow-wax has been imported whilst in seed, and there is a record of a growing plant found in Kensington, London in June 2000 at the base of a London Plane tree – only a few metres from a florist's shop! We have as yet no recent records from Sussex, but it could return and we ask you to look out for the Thorow-wax as a casual near cemeteries or churchyards. We would be very pleased to hear of any sightings.

Yellow-vetch
Vicia lutea

Pea family
Fabaceae

Habitat: Coastal shingle and cliffs, occasionally on grassy banks or chalk grassland
Height: Prostrate with rather trailing stems, can be 15cm high or 30cm long
Flowering: June to September
Status: Nationally Scarce and Scarce in Sussex
'Look-alike' plants: Yellow-vetch is the only British ground vetch with yellow flowers

Yellow-vetch is a prostrate, usually almost hairless annual, with hairs only on the pods. Its leaves are divided into three to seven pairs of small, narrowly oblong leaflets each about 1cm long, and blunt at the top with a small point at the tip. At the end of the leaf-stalk there is a small tendril, which is sometimes branched. The single flowers are 20 to 25mm long, very pale yellow and distinctly veined with pencil-coloured veins on the upright or 'standard' petal. The sepal teeth are unequal in size, the lower three being longer than the sepal tube. The 2 to 3cm pod is softly hairy, beaked and narrowly oblong, it contains four to eight 'peas'. Where the plants are growing on shingle, they can produce pods underground rather like peanuts. This occasionally happens to other members of the pea family.

In Sussex we have nearly a dozen sites for this plant, including shingle at Pagham, Widewater and Shoreham. In East Sussex it grows by the fence of the racecourse at Whitehawk, Brighton, and in rides in Friston Forest where it has been known for many years.

The first Sussex record of Yellow-vetch was in 1801, found by the renowned Sussex botanist William Borrer at Shoreham Harbour. A later botanist, the Reverend Arnold, in his *Sussex Flora* (1887) reported it "*On the pebbly beach between Shoreham Harbour and the sea*".

Yellow-vetch

Yellow-vetch is a plant of southern and western Europe and is at the northern edge of its range in Britain. In Britain it has not been seen at many of its sites in northern England and Scotland since the 1930s. There are reports of Yellow-vetch appearing in abundance after gorse scrub had been burnt; the warmth of the soil is obviously beneficial together with the increase in available light – so could the incidence of Yellow-vetch increase if Britain becomes warmer with climate change? Beyond Europe it is found also in north Africa, and Asia eastwards to Iran.

late summer

Bermuda-grass

Cynodon dactylon

Grass family
Poaceae (Graminae)

Habitat: Sandy ground in coastal areas of southern England
Height: 10-15cm
Flowering: August to September
Status: Red Data Book (Vulnerable) and Scarce in Sussex
'Look-alike' plants: Other introduced grasses with widely spreading flowering branches

This creeping perennial, with four to five spikes all arising at the same point (rather resembling the spokes of a broken umbrella), has been recorded as probably introduced. It is considered to be possibly native in long established colonies at Penzance and in Jersey (and therefore it was included in the *British Red Data Book* of endangered plants). The grass spreads rapidly in sandy ground near the sea, and is recorded in Sussex from Worthing and Brighton, but also in the grass around Hove Lagoon where it is known to have been established for at least for 50 years.

The Smooth Finger-grass *Digitaria ischaemum* also has flower spikes in rays or spokes and was recorded for the first time in Sussex in 2002, in a field near Bepton. This grass, unlike Bermuda-grass, has no stalk to the flower spikes and these prostrate rays form a 'lawn' in places. Bermuda-grass is one of the most widespread grasses in warmer areas and in Europe it can be found in the west and south and eastwards to the Ukraine. It is common in tropical areas as, for example in the Seychelles. It is resistant to trampling and survives on dry ground so may be used as lawn grass in warm dry climates, and could possibly increase in Britain in the future.

Birthwort

Aristolochia clematitis

Birthwort family
Aristolochiaceae

Habitat: Hedgerows. Introduced in Britain but occasionally naturalised near gardens
Height: 20-30cm
Flowering: June to September
Status: Scarce in Sussex
'Look-alike' plants: The curious horn shape of flowers makes this plant distinctive

Growing from an underground rhizome, Birthwort has numerous unbranched stems with broadly oval, heart-shaped 3-12cm long leaves and with leaf-stalks of about 10cm long. The leaf-edges are finely toothed. Pale yellow flowers grow in clusters of four to eight on short stalks. The tubes of the flowers are 2 to 3cm long and slightly curved, with a rounded swelling at the base and a flat oblong extension at the top. The whole plant is hairless and often has an unpleasant smell.

In Britain Birthwort is introduced, but in Sussex it has been known in Mayfield since 1892, which is an unusually long record of a naturalised plant.

The name 'Aristolochia' in ancient Greek means 'best birth' and the flower's tubular shape with a rounded base gives a similar appearance to the birth canal. Using the 'Doctrine of signatures' by which plants resembling parts of the body were used to treat those areas, this herb was given to help in childbirth. However, this plant does have abortive properties, so it may have been used for childbirth in more ancient times.

Birthwort has long been cultivated as a medicinal plant in physic gardens in England and in central and southern Europe, Russia and Asia Minor. In Mayfield in East Sussex the Birthwort grows by an old wall in West Street, and it could possibly have been originally associated with the old Knot Garden at the Bishop's Palace which was at the centre of Mayfield.

Bladderwort
Utricularia australis

Bladderwort family
Lentibulariaceae

Habitat: In ditches and ponds with acidic slow-moving water
Height: 10-20cm above water when in flower
Flowering: July to August
Status: Scarce in Sussex
'Look-alike' plants: Greater Bladderwort *Utricularia vulgaris*

Bladderwort does not have roots, in fact, this unassuming bloom is that of a carnivore! Each plant has submerged, oval leaves 2 to 2.5cm long that are delicately divided into thread-like, toothed segments; each tooth is tipped with one or several small bristles and on these submerged leaf-stalks are small (3mm) 'bladders'. These bladders are also tipped with bristles and with a special mechanism and enzymes for trapping and digesting tiny aquatic animals. The free-floating plants grow in water up to 1m in depth. When conditions are less favourable such as during the winter, when the ditches silt up, the water dries out or the ditch becomes overgrown with vegetation, Bladderwort can sink to the bottom to survive in damp mud for long periods until the situation improves. In late summer, if there is good sunshine warming the water, a stem grows above the water surface with two to six clear yellow flowers held 12 to 20cm high. The flowers have a spur and are double-lipped, the lower lip has a central reddish-brown raised knobble on the petals with brown lines and is flat and wavy. The flowers are pollinated by bees, but fruits are very rarely produced.

Bladderwort is not easily distinguished from the Greater Bladderwort, *Utricularia vulgaris*. Both species are unpredictable in flowering and in many years do not flower at all. If weather or water conditions are unfavourable Bladderwort may flower later in the year. At Amberley Wildbrooks Sussex

Bladderwort

Wildlife Trust nature reserve it has flowered in October. Without flowers the two species can not be separated in the field. When in flower the important characteristics of the Bladderwort are the longer, slender flower stalk, the flat lower lip and the lemon yellow colour of the flowers. (Greater Bladderwort has a stouter, shorter flower stalk 6-17mm, with lower lip usually folded down at the sides and a deeper, butter yellow colour).

In West Sussex Bladderwort has only been seen recently at Amberley Wildbrooks where it is found in several ditches. The survival of the plants here is dependant on regular dredging of these ditches. In East Sussex there are many more sites. These include ditches both north and south of the river bridge at Southease, reedbeds at Icklesham, near Camber Castle and at the Sussex Wildlife Trust nature reserves at Pett Pools and most recently after the restoration works at Filsham Reedbed near Hastings.

The Greater Bladderwort is much rarer in Sussex, with only one recent record from Pevensey Levels. This rarity is most likely explained by the plants' need for more alkaline water. As the pH of Amberley Wildbrooks has increased over the last century the number of Greater Bladderwort has

reduced. Bladderwort, meanwhile, has prospered at the site. The more recent records from Amberley are from the north-eastern side of the Brooks where the peat has been increasing and the water has a lower pH.

Bladderwort is scattered in Britain and Ireland, most common in the west and north. It also grows in Europe except the far north; in temperate Asia to China and Japan, tropical South Africa, Australia and New Zealand.

Bog Asphodel
Narthecium ossifragum

Lily family
Liliaceae

Habitat: In bogs and wet acid heathlands
Height: 5-30cm
Flowering: July to September
Status: Scarce in Sussex
'Look-alike' plants: No other plants have this appearance in this habitat

This beautiful flower of wet, peaty places has a hairless stalk and grows from a creeping rhizome. The lower leaves are flat, rigid, curved and have five veins, and the few, short, upper leaves sheath the stem. The flowering stem has a dense spike of golden yellow flowers at the top, each with six narrow 6-8mm long petals. When in flower the petals open to show the bright orange anthers on anther stalks (filaments) that are characteristically shaggy with long soft hairs.

Bog Asphodel grows in wet places with high rainfall, so there are times when insufficient insects are on the wing for pollination. This could be a potential problem for the Bog Asphodel, but it has developed a suitable technique for self pollination when no insect pollinators are around; after it rains, water is held inside the partly closed flowers by the hairs on the filaments to the level just below the anthers. This floats the pollen grains from the anthers onto the stigma at the centre of the flower.

Bog Asphodel still grows abundantly on the wet heaths, moors and mountains in the west and north of Britain and Ireland, but in Sussex these

Bog Asphodel

habitats are scarce. On Ashdown Forest, in East Sussex, Bog Asphodel is still widespread and in West Sussex we have some small remnant colonies. However these are endangered by the general drying and lowering of the water table, and in some cases by drainage. As heathland dries, scrub invades, and eventually woodland shades out the ground flora. This has been the case at Duncton Common, Heyshott Common and Hesworth Common where Bog Asphodel is still holding on, whilst plants in the Storrington and Wiggonholt areas have not been seen since 1980.

Bog Asphodel can be dangerous for grazing animals, and this was known to Linnaeus (1735) when he named the plant 'ossifragum' meaning 'broken bones'. Long after the time of Linnaeus it was discovered that the small flowers contain a phototropic chemical causing cattle grazing the flowers to become allergic to sunlight. Galloping about searching for shade on the unsuitable boggy ground could result in falls and broken bones.

Beyond Britain, Bog Asphodel grows in Arctic and sub-Arctic Europe from Iceland and the Faeroes eastwards to the Urals; also in the Alps, eastern Siberia, Arctic North America and Canada.

Bog Pimpernel
Anagallis tenella

Primrose family
Primulaceae

Habitat: Damp peaty and grassy places, and bogs
Height: 5-12cm
Flowering: June to early September
Status: Not included in *The Sussex Rare Plant Register*, but the number of plants is being monitored as a small decrease will warn of future rarity
'Look-alike' plants: Perennial Centaury and the occasional pink form of Scarlet Pimpernel

Although larger than the related Chaffweed, Bog Pimpernel is still a tiny plant creeping close to the soil with enchanting shell-pink flowers like upturned bells on slender 3cm stems. It is a native perennial with prostrate stems up to 20cm long. The leaves which are less than 1cm long are opposite, and the solitary flowers are 6 to 10mm across.

The Bog Pimpernel is found scattered over the British Isles, especially in the west, and grows also in Atlantic Europe and north Africa. In Sussex the records from the east are mainly from Ashdown Forest with a few records from the far north-west of West Sussex. A few lucky people have found this delightful flower growing on their lawns where these are damp and heathy. Drainage and destruction of habitat could further endanger this plant.

Broad-leaved Spurge

Euphorbia platyphyllos

Spurge family
Euphorbiaceae

Habitat: Formerly a weed of arable fields – now mostly on disturbed ground
Height: 15-60cm
Flowering: June to October
Status: Nationally Scarce
'Look-alike' plants: Some other spurges

Broad-leaved Spurge is an annual with unbranched stems and long alternate narrowly-oblong leaves up to 4cm long. The base of each leaf 'clasps' the stem with characteristic deep heart-shaped or rounded auricles, and the leaf is pointed at the tip. The umbel flower head usually has five rays above and sometimes lower branches below; it carries the green flowers with their green bracts underneath. The round fruiting capsule (2-3mm) is shallowly grooved with small warts on the surface.

This spurge is dependant on disturbance such as the ploughing fields. It was formerly locally frequent in the south and east of England, but now only local in a few of its old sites mainly due to the use of herbicide sprays in modern agriculture. In Sussex however, we still have a few sites. Most of these are from newly disturbed ground, and even at these sites the Spurge persisted for just two or three years at most. Only a third of Sussex sites for this plant were from lightly sown arable fields or field edges.

Wolley-Dod in his *Sussex Flora* (1937) describes the Broad-leaved Spurge as "*not uncommon in clayey cornfields*", and particularly quotes that it was a "*common cornfield weed at Warnham and Rusper*", "*Locally plentiful at Rudgewick*" and "*between Horsham and Slinfold in oats, in small quantity*".

Before 1970 this Spurge could, in many years, be found in stubble after the harvest, but a thorough more recent search in these areas did not refind any plants. However, during building in a field at nearby Itchingfield, West Sussex

Broad-leaved Spurge

a large pit was dug leaving a mound of soil. The following spring the whole mound was covered by Broad-leaved Spurge! The seeds must have been buried deep in the soil but remained viable once brought to the surface. The following year some of the spurge plants were still growing on the mound, mingled with other plant invaders, but the third year the Spurge had been crowded out – except that in the next few years an occasional Broad-leaved Spurge would appear in patches of newly dug soil in neighbouring gardens.

Broad-leaved Spurge grows through central and southern Europe from the Netherlands to northern Spain, Corsica, Sicily, and the west Caucasus.

Common Sea-lavender
Limonium vulgare (Statice limonium)

Thrift family
Plumbaginaceae

Habitat: Muddy saltmarshes
Height: 8-30cm
Flowering: July to October
Status: Not threatened (but related species are threatened and legally protected in Sussex – see text)
'Look-alike' plants: Other sea-lavender species

Common Sea-lavender is a perennial plant with a deep tap-root and branched stout woody stock. The dark green leaves have well marked veins, and they narrow to a long stalk: they can vary in shape. The upright, somewhat angular, flower stems are branched above the middle and the upper stems have dense spreading curved heads of flowers. The tiny, lavender-coloured flowers are set in two rows on the upper sides of the stems. The small, papery and persistent petals are broad and rounded and the anthers are yellow, helping to distinguish this from the Lax-flowered Sea-lavender.

Common Sea-lavender grows in mud at the sea edge of saltmarshes, anchored by the long tap-roots in the shifting soft mud, where it is often the dominant plant. When in full flower, growing at the edges of lagoons in the tidal zone, the sea-lavenders may be reflected in the sea water as the pools fill with the rising tide – a lovely sight on a sunny day with the colours of the flowers, sea and reflected sky and clouds.

Common Sea-lavender

In Sussex we have also three of the rarer species of sea-lavender: Lax-flowered Sea-lavender *Limonium humile* is present in several sites around Chichester Harbour, including Thorney Island – but is now extinct at Shoreham. This sea-lavender has longer, 'laxer', flowering stem branches with often paler flowers with reddish anthers. The leaf veins are less prominent than those of the Common Sea-lavender. Rock Sea-lavender *Limonium binervosum* is presumed extinct in West Sussex where it was last seen at Bosham in the 1950s. In East Sussex it was known as a cliff top plant at Cuckmere Haven early last century, but in 1936 was found on the beach below where a chunk of cliff had fallen! The plant has persisted there to this day on stable shingle. Rock Sea-lavender has flowering stems branched from near the base. It has been divided into six subspecies, which are distinct geographically in England. In East Sussex (and south east Kent) we have *Limonium binervosum* ssp. *binervosum*. At Rottingdean a large colony of a similar but larger and more shaggy sea-lavender, at one time thought to be Rock Sea-lavender is now identified as *Limonium procerum* of garden origin.

Common Sea-lavender

Planted in the garden of the White Horse Hotel in the early part of the last century it has spread vigorously along the cliff top and between the paving stones of the adjacent promenade.

Rottingdean Sea-lavender *Limonium hyblaeum,* also came from the same garden and is now also naturalised on the cliff beyond. The flower stems of this smaller Sea-lavender are usually less than 15 cm long and grow from a neat rosette of smaller leaves that do not overwinter. Introduced as a plant for rock gardens, it is grown in the municipal gardens in Brighton and other coastal towns, and recorded as an escape. In Britain this sea-lavender was first collected from Rottingdean (from which it now has its English name). At first botanists were very puzzled by it, but it was identified by a German botanist, M. Erben from Munich, who had collected specimens from Sicily, where it is native and endemic. It is now also known as a garden escape in Chile and in southern Australia!

Sea-lavenders are particularly difficult to identify, and some of the species also hybridise. *Limonium* taxonomy has presented many problems. Currently DNA tests are used as confirmation for difficult species and it is hoped that genetic studies may clarify some of the problems in the future.

Copse-bindweed
Fallopia dumetorum (Polygonum dumetorum)

Knotweed family
Polygonaceae

Habitat: Hedges on Bargate Beds sandstone and copse margins
Height: To 2m
Flowering: July to September
Status: Nationally Scarce
'Look-alike' plants: Black Bindweed and Russian Vine

Copse-bindweed is a climber with slender twining stems and narrowly triangular leaves. The small cream-coloured flowers occur on elongated stems growing from the junctions of the upper leaves with the main stem. These plants are more conspicuous in fruit, as each has a broad papery wing. The small triangular fruits are black and shiny.

In Sussex, Copse-bindweed is restricted to the north-west of West Sussex where the Bargate Beds sandstone forms a narrowly triangular deposit. The records of the plant through Rogate, Stedham, Trotton, Chithurst, Heyshott Green and Ambersham closely match the area of Bargate Beds as shown on the geological map of the area.

Copse-bindweed is an annual and is dependant on sufficient light for seed germination. The plants are very quickly shaded out, and will often reappear after an absence of many years following tree felling or coppicing. The seeds remain viable in the soil for many years, and regular coppicing gives ideal conditions for the continuing presence of the Copse-bindweed; the reduction of coppicing as woodland management in recent years is a threat to this nationally scarce plant.

Always rare in Britain, it has apparently decreased over the last 30 years. In Europe it is found north to southern Sweden, and eastwards across northern and western Asia.

131

Dwarf Elder (Danewort)

Sambucus ebulus

Honeysuckle family
Caprifoliaceae

Habitat: Waysides, rough and waste ground
Height: 60-120cm
Flowering: July to August
Status: Scarce in Sussex
'Look-alike' plants: Other elders, but distinguished by shape of flower head, growth habit and later flowering – or Common Valerian.

Dwarf Elder is a hairless, slightly foetid, perennial that has a creeping rhizome and many stout, erect, non-woody, furrowed green stems, often growing in a clump. The seven to 13 leaflets are between 5 and 15cm long, narrow and pointed, with sharply toothed margins. The leaves are more delicate and fern-like than those of the more common Elder shrub, and Dwarf Elder can be identified by its conspicuous leaf-like stipules at the junction of the leaflets with the main stems.

The flat-topped flower heads, 7 to 10cm across, have many small flowers that are pink in bud, and open to white with five tiny flat petals and purple anthers. These are pollinated by insects and the round fruits that appear in July or August are black.

Each September the stems, leaves and stalks to the fruits all turn blood red and the fruits will stain your fingers black. This may be the source of the legend in which the Dwarf Elder, or Danewort, grew spontaneously from the blood of slaughtered Danes. It was known to the Romans as a plant used as a remedy for gout, curing snake bites, and dyeing hair black. Remains of Dwarf Elder have been found in Neolithic settlements, and it was also used by the Anglo-Saxons. Another legend suggests that dosing children with Dwarf Elder

Dwarf Elder (Danewort)

suppressed their growth, and that poor families tried this, hoping to stunt the growth of their children in the days when dwarfs were valuable, as they could be sold to a travelling circus.

In Sussex the distribution of Dwarf Elder is much reduced, but the plants do persist in some sites at the foot of the Downs, especially on lane sides and field edges around the village of Harting in West Sussex and on a roadside and field edge at Edburton. In East Sussex there are recent records in a lane side hedge at Bishopstone.

Dwarf Elder has scattered records in Britain and Ireland. Further afield it is found from the Netherlands and Germany south to the Mediterranean, and from western Asia to the Himalayas.

Galingale
Cyperus longus

Sedge family
Cyperaceae

Habitat: Estuarine brackish tidal and coastal marshes. Also planted and naturalised by ponds and lakes
Height: To 1m
Flowering: August and September
Status: Nationally Scarce and Scarce in Sussex
'Look-alike' plants: Some other sedges and rushes

Galingale is a tall, smooth, branched perennial growing from a rhizome. The stems, as with all sedges, are triangular, with long leaves 4-7mm wide, and the flowers are in a branched umbel; longer leaf-like bracts overtop the flower head. Tiny greenish-brown flowers are followed by small, reddish-brown nut-like three cornered fruits 1mm wide, that are unlikely to ripen in Britain.

Although individual Galingale colonies spread rapidly by the rhizomes, many of the coastal colonies in southern Britain have been lost, mainly through drainage and change of agriculture. With decreasing grazing the sites have become invaded by scrub and dominant herbs, crowding out the Galingale.

In Sussex there are a few sites for this plant on the coastal marshes at Fishbourne, and also nine records from ponds and lakes. Galingale is widely available from aquatic garden centres and frequently planted as an ornamental. In the Channel Islands, where Galingale is called 'Han', it was in the past grown agriculturally because when dried the stems are sufficiently strong to use for ropes and cord. Matting for floors, tethers for cows, halters and collars were all made from Galingale in Jersey. Also known as 'Sweet Galingale', the rhizomes are aromatic and fragrant with the scent of Violets, and it was used in the preparation of perfume.

The name 'Galingale' is thought to be derived from Arabian and Chinese names of plants called 'Galanga' that are wild ginger in the Tropics and Far

Galingale

East. The aromatic roots of these plants are used in medicine and as a seasoning in cookery. Our plant, which also has an aromatic root is sometimes called 'English Galingale'. Anne Pratt in c.1855 writes of Galingale as "*Almost the only one of the sedges which has been used as food for man*", "*the succulent root is very sweet and fragrant . . . and it is a good stomachic*". It was the "*Galingale spyce*" of our ancestors and commonly used both for cookery and medicine. "*It helpeth the digestione, and both the savour and odour of the mouth if eaten*". Spenser in his *Faerie Queene* speaks of "*cheerful Galingale*" as one of the "*most prized*" herbs.

This is a Mediterranean plant with only a few scattered records from Lake Geneva, Switzerland, Bodensee, Germany, and southern England. A warmer climate could encourage its spread north, and possibly the fruits of the Galingale could ripen if we have hotter summers.

Golden-samphire
Inula crithmoides

Daisy family
Asteraceae

Habitat: Saltmarshes and occasionally on sea walls close to the sea
Height: 15-60cm
Flowering: July to October
Status: Nationally Scarce and Scarce in Sussex
'Look-alike' plants: Fleabane

This perennial, maritime, woody plant is branched with fleshy stems higher up the plant. The hairless, fleshy linear leaves are often three-toothed at the tip. The flower heads are about 2.5cm across and grow at the tops of the stems, with golden-yellow ray florets and orange-yellow central disc florets. Seed-set is very poor in years of cold summers, and seedlings are easily frosted in cold springs.

In Sussex, Golden-samphire is known only from Chichester Harbour growing in the saltmarshes, from the edges of muddy creeks or the banks at the back of the beach. Earlier Sussex records were all from the far west of West Sussex, the first from Bognor in 1828 when it was sold as a samphire for pickling.

Golden-samphire has a Mediterranean-Atlantic distribution. In Britain it is restricted to the southern and western coasts as far north as Suffolk in the east, and in the west to Anglesey, the Isle of Arran and the Mull of Kintyre.

Greater Water-parsnip

Sium latifolium

Carrot family
Apiaceae

Habitat: Species-rich wet ditches
Height: Up to 1.5m
Flowering: June to September
Status: Nationally Scarce and Scarce in Sussex
'Look-alike' plants: Lesser Water-parsnip

This large, handsome, perennial has a hollow grooved stem and long-stalked divided leaves up to 30cm long, each with about five leaflets all with finely toothed margins. When the leaves are submerged they are finely divided into linear segments. The flower head is a large rounded 'umbel', with many tiny white flowers each only 4mm across.

The 3mm fruits are distinctly longer than wide, strongly ridged with thick prominent ridges, and with persistent sepals – important characters to distinguish from the 'look-alike' Lesser Water-parsnip (which has fruits scarcely longer than wide, hairless and with low, slender ridges). The Lesser Water-parsnip also has darker green leaves with more deeply cut teeth to leaf margins. Larger plants of the Lesser have been mis-recorded for the Greater Water-parsnip.

Greater Water-parsnip can live submerged for some years without flowering. It produces abundant seed, but conditions are seldom good enough

Greater Water-parsnip

for seedling germination, indeed this plant has had a catastrophic decline due to drainage of habitat, the filling in of some ditches and widening of others. Greater Water-parsnip is intolerant of grazing and frequent cutting, but keeping the water in the ditches open by occasional clearance with a mechanical bucket provides the ideal management.

In West Sussex most sites for Greater Water-parsnip are in the Arun Valley. The plants are not long-lived but new plants appear at sites nearby along the ditches, so usually this plant is found as a single specimen. It is found at Amberley Wildbrooks, also Pulborough, Watersfield, North and South Stoke, Greatham and Wisborough Green, as well as ditchsides by the Adur at Henfield. In East Sussex there are just two records at Pevensey and Icklesham.

Greater Water-parsnip is widespread in Europe, except for the Mediterranean, and is absent in Portugal. It is rare in southern Fennoscandia, but extends into temperate Siberia – and is recorded in south eastern Australia.

Hay-scented Buckler-fern

Dryopteris aemula

Buckler-fern family
Dryopteridaceae

Habitat: Shady woods on the sandstone of the Tunbridge Wells Sand
Height: 15-50cm
Flowering: Spores ripen July to September
Status: Scarce in Sussex
'Look-alike' plants: Male-ferns and other Buckler-ferns

This fern is very scarce or most probably now extinct in West Sussex. A good colony near Chithurst was last seen in 1991, but unfortunately it has not been found in thorough searches of the area since. In East Sussex there are scattered records in the High Weald area, including in woods near Sharpthorne, Ashdown Forest, Dallington Forest, Crowborough and Frant.

The fronds of the Hay-scented Buckler-fern remain all year round, and are triangular and with three to four pinnae. The frond stalk, that is about as long as the blade, has numerous narrow red-brown scales, and the fronds are sprinkled with minute glands, mostly on the lower surface from which the scent of hay is released by volatile oils. Like all ferns, flowers are replaced by spores, and in buckler-ferns these are in clusters on the underside of the fronds, about half way between the mid-rib and the margins of the pinnae. They are covered by a shield-shaped tissue, giving these ferns their English name, as historically a 'buckler' was a small round shield with a central boss: this is the shape of the spore covers in shield-ferns such as the Hay-scented Buckler-fern.

Ivy-leaved Bellflower
Wahlenbergia hederacea

Bellflower family
Campanulaceae

Habitat: Wet heaths, woodland rides and streamsides on acid soils
Height: Trailing, up to 25cm long
Flowering: July to August
Status: Not Scarce
'Look-alike' plants: Harebell – but this has larger flowers, is taller, and is not a creeping, trailing plant

Ivy-leaved Bellflower is a small, slender, hairless and trailing perennial. Its stalked, lobed leaves are alternate on the stem and are 5 to 10mm long and kidney-shaped. The small, single, pale blue, bell-shaped flowers may be nodding or upright and are held above the leaves on slender thread-like stalks up to 4cm from the base of the leaves. The flowers are 6 to 10mm long, with three to five short pointed lobes which are about half as long as the tube. The sepals below are 2 to 3mm long with sharply pointed lobes, spread outwards, and these are much longer than the tube of the flower. The 3mm capsule is top-shaped and held upright.

Wahlenbergia is an intriguing Latin name for this group of Campanulas. The plants were named after Georg Wahlenberg (1780-1851), Professor of Botany at Uppsala, who was honoured for his studies of European plant geography.

Ivy-leaved Bellflower is found in woodland rides, by streams and on wet heaths on acid soils, and is locally frequent in Ashdown Forest, St. Leonard's Forest and woodlands around Worth and Buchan Park and in the Loder Valley. Elsewhere it is rare, but we have records from three wet 'heathy' lawns in gardens at Heathfield, on the Forest Ridge and the far west of Sussex near Wheatsheaf Common. In Britain and Ireland it is scattered on moors and heaths and is common in Wales and south west England. It is found in western Europe from Denmark to Spain and Portugal and in Dalmatia.

Ivy-leaved Crowfoot
Ranunculus hederaceus

Buttercup family
Ranunculaceae

Habitat: In mud at edges of ponds and ditches
Height: Low growing and in Sussex seldom more than 10cm high
Flowering: May to September
Status: Scarce in Sussex, and a plant for which Britain has special responsibility in European legislation
'Look-alike' plants: The very rare Three-lobed Crowfoot, and the larger Round-leaved Crowfoot

This tiny white-flowered buttercup is a creeping plant growing in mud. Occasionally the upper leaves are floating and more robust. The stalked opposite leaves are 1 to 1.5cm wide, kidney-shaped, deep green and often have darker markings. Ivy-leaved Crowfoot leaves are shallowly three to five lobed, with the broadest lobes at the base – this subtle difference distinguishes it from the Round-leaved Crowfoot in which the leaf lobes are narrowest at their base.

The minute starry flowers are 3 to 5mm across with narrow white petals which are hardly longer than the sepals below. The 1 to 2cm flower stalks are curved over and the fruits clustered in the centre of the flower are hairless with a short, blunt beak.

Since the 1960s there has been an apparent huge decline in this plant in East Sussex, with only one site in the last 15 years near Waldron. In West Sussex it is markedly more abundant with over ten sites which seem to have remained quite stable in the last 20 years. Ivy-leaved Crowfoot has been recorded from pond edges on West Heath Common, Cowdray Park, Petworth Park, Ebernoe Common, Coldwaltham and at Furnace Ponds, Slaugham. It is also recorded from ditches at Waltham Brooks and Amberley Wildbrooks.

It is assumed that the marked decrease of Ivy-leaved Crowfoot in East Sussex is due to loss of suitable habitats. A lack of grazing means less

Ivy-leaved Crowfoot

trampling by livestock resulting in fewer muddy ditch margins, but it is not clear why there should be such a contrast between the two counties. It is still considered to be frequent throughout the rest of Britain and Ireland, although it has been rather local for some time. It also grows in western Europe north to Denmark and southern Sweden.

The high level of protection for this plant is due to the reduction in its habitat across the whole of Europe. Although decreasing here too, Britain still has more than many other European countries where this plant used to grow – so they are looking to us to take care of our population.

Marsh Gentian
Gentiana pneumonanthe

Gentian family
Gentianaceae

Habitat: Wet heathland and damp acid grassland
Height: 10-40cm
Flowering: August to September
Status: Nationally Scarce and Scarce in Sussex
'Look-alike' plants: Unmistakable when in flower (but non-flowering are difficult to spot)

This beautiful perennial gentian has simple, usually erect stems with linear, blunt leaves between 1.5 and 4cm long. It usually has up to seven short-stalked flowers to each plant – these are rather crowded at the tops and in the axils of some stem leaves. The flowers are deep sky blue, usually with five green lines on the outside of the tube. This tube is broadly conical, 2.5 to 4cm long, opening out to five broadly oval petal lobes. The flowers are pollinated by Bumble-bees.

Marsh Gentian was first found in Sussex in St. Leonard's Forest in 1791. It was also known at Greatham Common, and Bog Common near Parham where it was last seen in 1968. Sadly, this was the last sighting in West Sussex and now it must be classified as extinct in that county. However, it is still one of the treasures of Ashdown Forest where gentians have maintained their numbers despite many pressures including forest fires, horse-riding, lack of grazing and picking. Marsh Gentians also persist, with careful management, on Chailey Common.

Marsh Gentian

Although Marsh Gentians are long lived perennials, the number of flowers varies considerably from year to year. For seed production and seedling establishment the plants require open habitats. The gradual establishment of scrub and eventually birch trees at a site causes the habitat to become increasingly dry, conditions that this species cannot tolerate. Several of our Sussex sites have been lost due to vegetation encroachment. This happened at Bog Common and some older East Sussex sites. Warm weather can increase the flowering, and in cool summers the non-flowering plants can be very difficult to find.

As a plant of acid grassland and heathland, Marsh Gentian often grows with Cross-Leaved Heath *Erica tetralix* and heathland grasses. The loss of sites, especially in northern England, has been mainly through the destruction of habitat – by ploughing, drainage or tree planting for forestry; and also because there are now fewer grazing animals on these habitats across the country.

On the Ashdown Forest in 2000 in an intensive survey the flowering spikes were counted, totalling around 700. We are fortunate in East Sussex to have good colonies, but continued monitoring and management are vital for the future existence of the Marsh Gentian in Sussex – we must ensure that our children and grandchildren can still have the joy of seeing open heathland studded with blue 'trumpets' of Marsh Gentian in late summer and early autumn.

Marsh Gentian grows over much of Europe from southern Scandinavia to the mountains of Spain, Italy and the Balkans, and east to central Asia. However, in all of these areas it is showing similar losses in numbers of sites and size of populations as in Sussex.

Marsh St. John's-wort

Hypericum elodes

St. John's-wort family
Clusiaceae

Habitat: Pondsides, streamsides and on boggy or acid marsh soils
Height: To 30cm
Flowering: June to September
Status: Scarce in Sussex
'Look-alike' plants: Other St. John's-worts

Marsh St. John's-wort is a low-growing, densely velvety-hairy perennial spreading with underground stolons. The soft stems root from the junctions with the lower leaves. The rounded, oblong or heart-shaped leaves have no stalks. The flowers are about 1.5cm across, and the sepals below have fine red or purplish glandular teeth. When growing well, Marsh St. John's-wort forms large tufted cushions often at the water's edge, a lovely sight on a sunny day. The dense soft hairs prevent the plant getting wet when submerged.

Marsh St. John's-wort was recorded first in Sussex in 1789, when it was said to be common in the brooks of the Weald. In 1937 Wolley-Dod in his *Sussex Flora* cited over 40 Sussex localities, but it has now declined to just a few sites, mainly due to pond drainage and loss of suitable habitats. Three of the remaining sites are from pond edges in West Sussex, at Milland, near Horsham and at Spruce Hill. In East Sussex there are eight recent records, including Ashdown Forest, Heathfield and Smockfarthing Lake. It is also at Piltdown Pond, where unfortunately it is threatened by aggressive Floating Pennywort, an invasive species from North America.

We do not have records of Marsh St. John's-wort having been used medicinally, but many species in the large worldwide St. John's-wort family are noted for medicinal properties. Possibly the best known is the Common St. John's-wort, *Hypericum perforatum*. This also grows in Sussex in meadows,

Marsh St. John's-wort

field edges and on sunny banks, and it has been used in the treatment of wounds at least since the time of Dioscorides (512B.C.)

All members of the St. John's-wort family were also thought to be powerful against evil spirits and sprays were commonly hung over the doors of houses and churches on the eve of St. John's Day (24th June). For many years is has been known as an anti-depressant, a use that has recently been highlighted in the media.

In Europe the plant became closely associated with the early Crusaders who used the herb to treat bleeding on the battlefield. All the St. John's-worts contain an essential oil and red pigment used for healing wounds and inhibiting inflammation. The powdered herb was also given as an infusion for the treatment of urinary complaints and for coughs and colds. When the stem of the flowering plant is steeped in olive oil and left in sunlight the oil is coloured red and this is used today in massage treatments.

Marsh St. John's-wort is still locally frequent in west and south Britain where suitable habitats remain, and is occasionally found in western Europe from Portugal to Germany, Italy and the Azores.

Marsh-mallow
Althea officinalis

Mallow family
Malvaceae

Habitat: Coastal and marshy
Height: 1-1.5m
Flowering: August and September
Status: Locally abundant
'Look-alike' plants: Common Mallow and Tree-mallow (see page 181)

This beautiful plant is found growing in slightly saline, marshy sites near the sea – and here it often grows in profusion. It is tall, from 1-1.5m and softly hairy. The velvet-textured leaves are slightly lobed, and are sometimes folded like a fan. The plant has attractive pale pink flowers each about 4cm in diameter, and growing in short-stalked clusters of up to three flowers.

Sixty years ago, Marsh-mallow was considered to be a rather common plant in marshes near the sea, but it is now less common and more recently is only recorded from 20 sites in Sussex. Most records are near the sea and it is often found growing just behind the beach or by the sea wall. Marsh-mallow also grows along rivers and it has been found as far inland as Arundel, on the banks of the River Arun – but it has rarely only been seen on the River Adur. In East Sussex it grows in the Cuckmere Valley, near the Seven Sisters Country Park visitor centre, but has not been recorded from the River Ouse.

Marsh-mallow

The pink and white sweets that we know as 'Marsh-mallows' are the modern version of the Marsh-mallow sweets made in the time of Elizabeth I. The roots of the Marsh-mallow plant were described by Gerard in his *Herball* in 1597 as *"thicky tough white within"* and *"containing a clammie and slimie juice"*. This mucilaginous gel thickens in water – as they discovered in Elizabethan times – to become *"as if it were jelly"*. The *officinalis* in the Latin name for this plant indicates that it was used in medicine in the past, and it was indeed sold by apothecaries. Housewives would grow Marsh-mallow in their physic garden to be used for poultices, ointments and sweetmeats. Whooping cough is one of the long list of ailments for which the sweets were used. Modern Marsh-mallows keep the name but have no connection to our *Althea officinalis* and are not reputed to have healing properties!

In Sussex this attractive plant can be seen at Amberley Wildbrooks, on the North side of the wall around Seven Sisters Visitor Centre at Exceat and it also grows in abundance at Rye Harbour Local Nature Reserve.

The plant's scattered distribution extends across southern England, and it can also be seen in central Europe and as far away as north Africa and western Asia.

Meadow Thistle
Cirsium dissectum

Daisy family
Asteraceae

Habitat: Fens and the margins of bogs on peat
Height: 20-60cm
Flowering: June to August
Status: Scarce in Sussex
'Look-alike' plants: Other thistles, but distinguished by the shape and teeth of the leaves

Meadow Thistle is a perennial with usually unbranched cottony stems and a single flowering head. The leaves are green and hairy on the upper surface, and whitish with cottony hairs on the lower surface. The leaves can be up to 25cm long – including the long stalk – lance-shaped, wavy edged and the margins have soft prickles. The flower heads are ovoid between 2 and 2.5cm wide, purplish and with spiny dark red-purple bracts below the florets. The seeds have long, silky, very white hairs at their tops.

In Sussex we have less than ten recent sites, all from wet acid meadows such as those at Ashington, Ditchling Common, Chailey, Wivelsfield and Duddleswell. The number of Sussex sites is restricted by the relatively small and decreasing number of habitats suitable for the Meadow Thistle, due to drainage and increased building.

Meadow Thistle

In Britain, Meadow Thistle is a plant of the south and west – found in southern and south west England, south Wales, south western Scotland and throughout Ireland. Losses of this species in south east England in the last 40 years are largely due to drainage and shading of heathland caused by successive colonisation by scrub and woodland.

Meadow Thistle is found in western Europe from Spain to the Netherlands and north west Germany.

Moon Carrot
Seseli libanotis

Carrot family
Apiaceae

Habitat: Chalk grassland near the sea
Height: 30cm-1.2m
Flowering: July to September
Status: Red Data Book (Vulnerable) and Scarce in Sussex
'Look-alike' plants: Wild Carrot and Sea Carrot, but they differ from Moon Carrot in leaves and fruiting stems

Moon Carrot is a sturdy biennial or perennial with solid stems. The leaves are about 10cm long, divided two or three times into oblong lobes. The flower heads are terminal umbels measuring 3 to 6cm across with 15 to 30 rays and minute white flowers that are just 1 to 1.5mm across with petals that are hairy on the back. Under the flowers and where the rays join the stem there are narrow, green, pointed bracts. The oval fruits are 3mm long and the ray stems remain straight in fruit, unlike in the 'look-alike' Wild Carrot where the rays curve in fruit, giving the look of a small bird's nest. In the Sea Carrot the rays are very bristly but do not curve in fruit. All the carrots are related to our vegetable carrot.

On the East Sussex cliff tops the sea winds keep the Moon Carrot low growing and they often come into flower while the main stem is short and

Moon Carrot

leaves surround the compact umbel of white flowers, giving the Moon Carrot at this stage a distinct resemblance to cauliflowers dotted on the cliff top turf. The flowers are then very white and are said to be conspicuous by moonlight, hence the name Moon Carrot.

Moon Carrot is known from only six localities in England, one of which is in East Sussex where it grows in grassland on the coastal chalk between Hope Gap and Eastbourne. The plants are vulnerable to rabbit grazing, but the current management – sheep and cattle grazing early in the year, together with occasional topping of the sward after seed set to prevent it becoming too rank – appears to be suitable.

In Europe Moon Carrot has a wide distribution from Spain northwards, the Benelux countries and Fennoscandia and east to Poland, Russia and Bulgaria. It also grows in north Africa and south west Asia. High mountain meadows are the usual habitat of Moon Carrot in continental Europe.

Night-flowering Catchfly
Silene noctiflora

Pink family
Caryophyllaceae

Habitat: Arable fields on soils with good drainage – chalk or sand
Height: 15-35cm
Flowering: June to August
Status: Not Scarce
'Look-alike' plants: Nottingham Catchfly

Night-flowering Catchfly is a hairy annual which is sticky with glands on the upper half of the plant, and aphids and other small flying insects become trapped by these sticky hairs. The 5 to 10cm leaves are oval or lanceolate, the lower narrowed to a stalk, the upper stalkless and narrowly spear-shaped and very sharply pointed. The flowers are clustered at the top of the stems. At flowering time the woolly, sticky calyx is long and slender, and approximately 2cm long, cylindrical with ten broad green ridges and five tender teeth at the top. Later as they ripen the calyces become oval and rounded. The green ridges are then prominent and between these the calyx is whiteish with branched green veins with the teeth at the top re-curved.

The plant's germination and flowering time depend on the timing of the ploughing of the field. The seeds are long-lived in the soil, but for good germination they are dependant on hot sunny weather. In cool wet summers no flowers may germinate. In a good year there can be many hundreds of plants and, as the buds open during the day, the petals are tightly rolled

Night-flowering Catchfly

showing the deep yellow colour of the petal undersides. After dusk some of the petals open flat, showing the pale dusty pink of their top surface, deeply notched to nearly half their length. The stamens and the stigmas appear on successive evenings and in fine weather the flowers may refurl during the day and open again on two or three successive evenings: ensuring pollination by moths – possibly the Silver Y moth. By midnight the open flowers are already refurled. When the flowers open they are very fragrant and an older name for this flower was in fact Night-scented Catchfly.

Although now not considered to be Nationally Scarce the Night-flowering Catchfly has declined considerably since 1950. In Sussex too there has been a significant decrease in the last 25 years, so it should be carefully monitored over the next years. At present we have 11 post-1986 records with four localities in West Sussex and nine in East Sussex. In West Sussex it has been found in arable fields at Lavant, in a field of rape in Sutton, and in an arable field north of Whiteways. The East Sussex records come from fields at

Night-flowering Catchfly

Moulescoomb, Southease, Denton and South Heighton; and also from setaside at Jevington. Changes in agricultural practice, and in particular the ploughing and re-planting of arable fields at the end of the summer immediately after the harvest of the previous crop has prevented this late flowering species from setting seed. The establishment of 'conservation headlands' considerably benefits the Night-flowering Catchfly.

This species is still widespread in Europe and Asia, but it is rare in northern Europe and in the Mediterranean.

Oblong-leaved Sundew
Drosera intermedia

Sundew family
Droseraceae

Habitat: Damp heaths and in wet sphagnum moss on sand or peat
Height: 5-10cm
Flowering: June to August
Status: Scarce in Sussex
'Look-alike' plants: Round-leaved Sundew

Oblong-leaved Sundew is an insectivorous plant growing in bare boggy patches, or along the edges of paths and tracks on the peaty soils of acid heaths. The slender stems, with small white flowers arise in mid to late summer. While the flowers are very short lived, all the year round the densely glandular leaves are conspicuous with their reddish colour and fringe of long glandular hairs. The oblong leaf blades are about 1cm long and gradually narrowed to a smooth hairless leaf stalk. The hairs on the blade hold tiny 'dew drops' from the glands, and these leaves are finely adapted to trapping insects. Small insects are trapped by the sticky dew drops, then the leaves fold around the prey. Enzymes from the glandular hairs in time digest the insect, and this supplies the sundew with valuable nitrogen, that is often scarce in the poor soils on which the Oblong-leaved Sundew grows.

Oblong-leaved Sundew

This sundew grows in scattered localities through the British Isles, mainly in the west, where suitable habitats exist. It is less frequent than the Round-leaved Sundew, which is distinguished by having longer stalks with smaller and almost circular leaves.

In earlier times the tiny 'dew drops' of clear, sticky liquid from the glandular hairs on the leaves of the Oblong-leaved Sundew attracted attention, and the liquid was used against sunburn and freckles. The juice from boiling the leaves in asses' milk was given to children with whooping cough, or distilled in wine to make *Rosa solis* the "*dew of the sun*".

Oblong-leaved Sundew grows in west and central Europe and north to Norway, Sweden and Finland and it is also found in Asia Minor.

Pyramidal Orchid
Anacamptis pyramidalis

Orchid family
Orchidaceae

Habitat: Chalk grassland
Height: 20-60cm
Flowering: Late June to mid August
Status: Not Scarce
'Look-alike' plants: The pyramidal shape of this orchid as the early flowers open makes it distinctive

The Pyramidal Orchid is a conspicuous orchid, known for its ability to colonise new areas although it is normally persistent in its old sites. It is a plant of the downland and is common in Sussex along the length of the chalk ridge in both East and West Sussex.

The Pyramidal Orchid has a slender stem, usually around 20cm tall – but it can measure 60cm with three or four narrow pointed basal leaves, that may be shrivelled by flowering time. There are around six narrow sheathing stem leaves above the rosette. The short flower spike, 2 to 5cm in height, is densely packed with tiny flowers. The lower flowers open first, giving the spike its characteristic pyramid shape. As more flowers open the spike becomes more oval and rounded at the top. The flowers are most often bright pink, rosy-purple in bud, becoming paler as they open. However they may be variable from very pale pink to darkish red, and occasionally albino.

Pyramidal Orchid

The two lateral sepals of the tiny flowers spread outwards, and the upper sepal and two upper petals are rounded to form a small, loose head. The lip has three, well-divided, equal lobes that are rounded and spreading. There is a very long, straight, thick spur. Butterflies, moths, and other insects will visit the flowers and the pollination mechanism is very detailed and complex. It is a successful system resulting in a very high percentage of seed set.

Pyramidal Orchids are widely distributed in southern England, the Midlands, Wales and the Isle of Man, throughout Ireland and on the western seaboard of Scotland. In western Britain and Ireland this plant is also found on calcareous sand dunes. It is widespread in Europe and is found north to southern Scandinavia and central Russia. It also occurs even further afield in west Asia and north Africa.

Pyramidal Orchids are widespread at Camber Sands and at Sussex Wildlife Trust nature reserve The Malling Downs, particularly at Oxteddle Bottom where 30,000 spikes were recorded in 2002.

Ray's Knotgrass

Polygonum oxyspermum (Polygonum raii)

Knotweed family
Polygonaceae

Habitat: On sandy beaches, and similar to Sea Knotgrass
Height: Prostrate, mat-forming stems to 80cm along the sand
Flowering: June to October
Status: Scarce in Sussex
'Look-alike' plants: Sea Knotgrass (see page 172)

Ray's Knotgrass is very similar to Sea Knotgrass, with which it is often confused. Slightly larger and more straggly, Ray's Knotgrass has very slightly larger pink or white flowers approximately 3mm wide. The light brown, shiny, nut-like fruits extend beyond the persistent remnants of the flower, distinguishing Ray's from Sea Knotgrass.

Both the Sea and Ray's Knotgrasses grow in similar habitats, quite frequently growing together – as they were on the beach by Brighton Marina, so that both colonies were destroyed by the same storm there in 1996. It is a rare plant in Sussex with five post-1986 records from West Sussex and two from East Sussex.

Ray's Knotgrass is an Atlantic species, scattered and decreasing around the western coasts of Britain, Ireland and the other islands. It is also found on coasts of Europe from Norway to northern France.

This Knotgrass is named after the Reverend John Ray (1627-1705) the British botanist who travelled widely through Britain cataloguing wild plants. He was in Sussex in 1662 and Sussex records in his writings name many plants – for many these were the first records for the counties.

Red Hemp-nettle
Galeopsis angustifolia

Dead-nettle family
Lamiaceae

Habitat: Two distinct habitats – coastal sands, and inland arable fields on chalk or sand
Height: 10-30cm
Flowering: July to October
Status: Nationally Scarce and Scarce in Sussex
'Look-alike' plants: Red Dead-nettle

Red Hemp-nettle is a sparse annual, which has narrow linear or spear-shaped leaves with one to four teeth on each side. The flowers are in crowded whorls, both at the top of the stem and also where side-branches join the stem. Each individual flower is tubular, rosy-purple and 1.5 to 2.5cm long, much longer than the slightly hairy sepals. The flowers are two-lipped, with the upper helmet-shaped and the lower three-lobed.

The Red Hemp-nettle competes poorly with dense, heavily-fertilised crops and has thus decreased drastically from arable habitats throughout England. In Sussex it is also now very rare as an arable weed, only found at Malling Down and Alciston in East Sussex. However it still has several coastal sites, particularly Rye and Pagham harbours. The size of the coastal populations fluctuate markedly from year to year – possibly the plant needs warm sunshine in late summer the previous year to ensure good seed set for the spring.

Red Hemp-nettle is found through central and southern Europe, and east to Poland, Bosnia and Bulgaria.

Red Star-thistle

Centaurea calcitrapa

Daisy family
Asteraceae (Compositae)

Habitat: Possibly native in Sussex on dry banks on the chalk. Most likely casual in other habitats
Height: 15-60cm
Flowering: July to September
Status: Red Data Book (Vulnerable) and Scarce in Sussex
'Look-alike' plants: Other purple-red thistles with spiny leaves

Red Star-thistle is a biennial with a stout tap-root and branched erect grooved flower stems. The stem leaves, up to 8cm long, are deeply cut into narrow lobes, sparsely hairy but with bristle points at the tips. The flower heads are 8 to 10cm across, and the younger branches successively overtop the older heads to give an open spreading shrubby plant. Below the petals, the flower head has overlapping bracts each with a stout, spreading, yellow, grooved spine 2.5cm long, which gives the name 'Star' Thistle. The individual florets are pale red-purple, and the flowers are pollinated by visiting bees and flies.

The Red Star-thistle has declined throughout Britain. Formerly it was a weed of arable fields, imported with Lucerne seed from southern France and Italy. It became extinct as an arable weed when the crop seed was cleaned more efficiently. Lucerne was introduced around 1650, but earlier records show that the Red Star-thistle was known in Britain from waste ground before that date.

In Sussex the Red Star-thistle is now found mostly in East Sussex and the main colonies are those in the Cuckmere Valley at Exceat, near the bus stop opposite the barn and in the Seven Sisters Country Park. Older records reported by the botanist Wolley-Dod in his *Sussex Flora* include Brighton,

Red Star-thistle

where it was described as "*a most conspicuous weed*" in 1877. It has also been recorded at Roedean and abundant on the cliffs at Rottingdean. In all there are nearly 20 sites for this species in Sussex – only four of which are in West Sussex, including a colony in a disused chalk pit at Newtimber and a spreading colony on Southwick Hill that is thought to be introduced.

The Red Star-thistle is widespread in southern Europe, including the Mediterranean islands, and from Spain east to Russia and north to southern England. It also grows in north Africa, the Canary Islands and west Asia. It flourishes in a Mediterranean climate, and in Sussex the number of flowering plants fluctuates from year to year depending on the weather. This could be another plant that might increase if global warming gives warmer, drier summers.

Round-headed Rampion

Phyteuma orbiculare

Bellflower family
Campanulaceae

Habitat: Downland
Height: 5-40cm
Flowering: July to September
Status: Rare in Britain but locally abundant on the Sussex Downs
'Look-alike' plants: Knapweeds and Cornflower

The local name for this flower is the Pride of Sussex, as our chalk downland was once famed for colonies of these deep blue flower heads in late summer. The flower stalks grow from a 'rosette' of leaves, and the plants can range from as short as 5cm when grazed, to their more usual height of 40cm. The globular blue flower heads on single almost leafless stems are eye-catching and prominent amongst the other flowers of the downland slopes.

This chalk grassland plant grows along the South Downs in both East and West Sussex where there is still old downland turf. In Britain, it is restricted to the chalk Downs of south east England. Before the Second World War it was often abundant along the South Downs. However, since then much downland has been ploughed and the soil enriched with fertilizers. Furthermore, fewer sheep are now kept on the Downs so the impact of grazing has reduced, leading to more scrub, coarse grasses encroaching on the flower rich chalk turf.

Round-headed Rampion

Myxomatosis, which has decimated rabbit populations, has also been an influence. Thus in the last 60 years, Round-headed Rampion numbers have dwindled. It has not been seen in Kent since 1940, but does still grow on some of the Surrey Downs. It is now listed as a scarce plant in Britain.

The colourful Six-spot Burnet Moth, with crimson spots, is often found with this rampion and sometimes the yellow chrysalis cases are found on the stems. It is possible that when the proposed South Downs National Park is designated, some of the arable fields on the Downs may be returned to grassland. With careful management downland turf species, including the Round-headed Rampion, could thrive again.

Meanwhile look for it on our downland slopes in July and August. You should be able to see it in the following Sussex Wildlife Trust nature reserves: Levin Down, Ditchling Beacon and Malling Downs.

The Round-headed Rampion is widespread in the mountain meadows in south central Europe – but in Sussex we are lucky to still see areas of downland turf dotted with the compact blue flowers. Here it is a treasure of the Downs well deserving its local name.

Sea-holly

Eryngium maritimum

Carrot family
Apiaceae

Habitat: Coastal sands and shingle
Height: 30-50cm
Flowering: July to August
Status: Scarce in Sussex
'Look-alike' plants: Only the very rare Field Eryngo

Sea-holly is no relative of our familiar red-berried Holly, but is a native perennial plant in the carrot family with an unusual structure and very attractive blue-green colouring. It is smooth, hairless and branched with basal leaves 5 to 12cm across. These lower leaves are stalked, almost rounded and three-lobed. The stem leaves are unstalked, closely attached to the stem and shaped like a Holly leaf. All the leaves have thickened margins with prickly, spiny teeth. The oval heads of the numerous flower heads are 1.5 to 2.5cm across with spiny, toothed bracts which are often purple-blue and longer than the blue flowers.

In Sussex the Sea-holly is classified as 'Scarce' with the numbers decreasing. There are four sites in total, two in the far east of Sussex at Pett Level and Camber Golf Course, and two in the far west coastline on dunes at Climping and East Head. These colonies must be monitored in case of further decline.

Sea-holly

The Sea-holly is a useful plant for stabilising dunes, and in Holland it has been planted for this reason on newly constructed dunes. There the introduced plants are protected by legislation and it is illegal to pick any part of the Sea-holly.

The spongy roots of the Sea-holly, like those of its rarer relative the Field Eryngo, *Eryngium campestre,* were formerly used in medicine for diseases of the bladder and as a tonic. They were made into a sweetmeat called *Eryngo.* The candied roots were called "*kissing comfits*" and are thought to have been the "*eringoes*" eaten by Falstaff, described by Shakespeare in *The Merry Wives of Windsor.*

The Sea-holly grows along the Atlantic coasts of Europe from Portugal to southern Scandinavia, through the Mediterranean and the Black Sea. In Britain it has now mostly gone from the coasts of Scotland and northern England, but is found still along the coasts of southern England where there are suitable habitats.

Sea-kale
Crambe maritima

Cabbage family
Brassicaceae

Habitat: On (or very near to) shingle beaches
Height: 40-60cm
Flowering: June to August
Status: Nationally Scarce
'Look-alike' plants: Very distinctive

This handsome branched perennial plant is smooth surfaced with rather waxy blue-green, crisp, crinkly and curly, long-stalked leaves. The branched fleshy root stock is adapted to survival buried under shingle or deep sand, and the sprouting stems can be 2 to 3cm thick. The white petalled green-clawed flowers, nearly 1cm across, are followed by rounded or oval 'ball' fruits 12 to 14mm by 8mm on elongating fruiting stems. The fruits can float for many days in sea water to colonise new areas of beach.

Before a variety of vegetables was readily available all the year round, as now, Sea-kale was prized as a wild food. It was collected from the coasts and sold in town markets, and it is claimed that some of the finest Sea-kale to be sold at Covent Garden was gathered in quantity from Pevensey Beach. Now that plants from the wild are no longer collected for food, the Sea-kale has increased on Sussex shingles. For use as a vegetable, shingle (or sand) was heaped around the young shoots as this appeared to blanche out the bitterness, and they were then served like asparagus. Some enterprising gardeners with suitable gardens cultivate Sea-kale today for use in cooking. The collection of Sea-kale in the past has had a large impact on the population of the plant on our beaches, and it is recorded that when the

Sea-kale

coast at Pevensey was a forbidden area after the First World War, in the summer of 1920, the beach there was "*a beautiful sight, the flowers covering the shingle with a foam of white and cream*". That length of beach has now sadly been built over with bungalows. Miller in his *Gardener's Dictionary* of 1731 recorded that the wild plant was found in great plenty on the Sussex coast.

This is a particularly English vegetable – the French called it "*the sea-cabbage of England*" but in Sussex it was reported that it was "*preferred to any of the cabbage kind*". We are fortunate that we can still see the Sea-kale flowering on a number of shingle beaches, as at West Wittering, Shoreham, Norman's Bay and near Eastbourne. We must surely protect the native flora on our remaining vegetated shingle beaches.

Sea-kale is restricted in distribution to Britain, northern France and the Baltic coasts with small populations in northern Spain, Ireland and around the Black Sea. In Britain there are records from around the coast and in Sussex we have over 20 sites where it grows.

Sea Knotgrass
Polygonum maritimum

Knotweed family
Polygonaceae

Habitat: Close to the sea above the high tide mark in fine shingle or in sand
Height: Mat-forming, with prostrate stems to 25cm
Flowering: June to October
Status: Red Data Book (Endangered), Schedule 8 and Scarce in Sussex
'Look-alike' plants: Ray's Knotgrass (see page 162)

Sea Knotgrass is a mat-forming blue-green shiny perennial, with one to four minute pink or white flowers between 2 to 2.5mm in size. The nut-like shiny perennial brown fruits remain almost hidden and sheathed, a character distinguishing Sea Knotgrass from the 'look-alike' plant Ray's Knotgrass.

Sea Knotgrass was first found in Sussex in 1992 when 16 plants were discovered near Brighton Marina. In the following two years the colony increased to 94 plants, but was already declining when in 1996 a fierce storm destroyed the remaining plants. None have been found there since then, despite annual searches. However, a second Sussex site was found in West Sussex at West Wittering, that survived for only a year, and a new small colony was found nearby at East Head in 2002.

Sea Knotgrass

In southern England only six colonies were surviving along the coast in 1999 – Sea Knotgrass has always been rare and vulnerable to being destroyed by storms and shifting shingle. Over-enthusiastic beach maintenance can be a threat, but the Brighton Marina site, the most easterly site – was on a beach recently reconstructed by sea defence works.

It seems that seeds of Sea Knotgrass remain viable and resistant to salt for some years in the sand, as colonies do reappear at old sites from time to time, but in Britain the pattern for this plant has been of sporadic occurrences followed by years when it appears to be absent. In 1962 it was only known in south west Britain and its new sites show a considerable spread to the east – presumably spurred on by the mild winters of recent years.

Sea Knotgrass is found throughout Europe, on the Black Sea, Mediterranean and Atlantic coasts, and northwards to Belgium.

Six-stamened Waterwort

Elatine hexandra

Waterwort family
Elatinaceae

Habitat: On wet mud in pond edges
Height: 2.5-6cm
Flowering: July to September
Status: Nationally Scarce and Scarce in Sussex
'Look-alike' plants: Water Starworts

This tiny slender plant creeps on the mud at pond edges; new roots grow from the stem at junctions with the leaves, and plants also spread by seed. The small leaves are opposite, spatula-shaped and with a short stalk. The tiny pink flowers are 1 to 2mm across, have short stalks and usually have three petals and six stamens. A similar plant, Eight-stamened Waterwort also grows in these habitats, but it was last seen in Sussex in 1944 – so is presumed now to be extinct in our counties.

Six-stamened Waterwort can also be found at the edges of lakes and reservoirs where there is a suitable shelving muddy floor. The plants are often submerged and can sometimes flower under water that is sufficiently shallow for light to penetrate. Non-flowering plants have been recorded at depths of 2m; these plants do not have open flowers with petals but they can produce seed by self-pollination.

The seeds of the Six-stamened Waterwort are dispersed by water, possibly also by birds, and they are long-lived in the mud. If the water is drained they germinate rapidly and in a few days the small plants can be flowering profusely. Some years ago this happened in East Sussex at Sheffield Mill Pond when it was drained one early autumn; the exposed mud was carpeted with the tiny flowers of the waterwort, and for a few days they could be seen from some distance as a pink haze.

Six-stamened Waterwort

Clean unpolluted water, muddy edges and the water depth are important factors for the survival of this waterwort. It can tolerate a wide range of water chemistry, but is not found in very chalky waters. Although it can live submerged for some years, it is rarely seen where pond levels have been raised permanently for angling and the shallow muddy pond edges have been lost. These higher water levels can also encourage the growth of aggressive invasive alien waterweeds – for example, Floating Pennywort (which is now present at Piltdown Pond). These species could crowd out the Six-stamened Waterwort found at this site.

In Sussex we still have four recent records of this waterwort in three sites at Forest Mere near Liphook, Shillinglee Lake and Piltdown Pond, but in all of these its survival could be threatened by changes in water level and loss of shallow muddy edges to the water.

In Europe Six-stamened Waterwort occurs from Norway to Spain and northern Italy and the Azores.

Slender Hare's-ear
Bupleurum tenuissimum

Carrot family
Apiaceae

Habitat: On dunes, sea walls and the banks of coastal paths, brackish pastures and landward edges of salt marshes
Height: 25cm
Flowering: July to September
Status: Scarce in Britain, but in Sussex many records from along the coast – mainly in West Sussex
'Look-alike' plants: Easily distinguished from the Thorow-wax by its small size, narrow leaves and coastal habitat

This often inconspicuous plant is a greyish-green annual with slim, wiry branched stems. The 1 to 5cm long leaves are narrow and linear. The characteristic look of the plant is given by its bracteoles, that are longer than the slender groups of tiny flowers on one to three rays, and the individual 1mm yellowish flowers are followed by 2mm black, rounded fruits.

This plant is noticeably more abundant in years following hot dry weather from July through to early autumn, enabling good seed production for the following year. 2002 was an excellent year for this plant, with records in four new localities in West Sussex, and larger populations in some of the known sites also. Slender Hare's-ear is one of the plants that could possibly increase again through the effects of global warming in future years.

In 1937 Sussex botanist Wolley-Dod wrote *"the records throughout the length of the coast from Thorney to Midrips are too numerous to detail"*. Nearly 70 years later Slender Hare's-ear is still reasonably frequent around Chichester Harbour and Pagham. Eastwards from there we have no sites until Southease; an isolated record from Cuckmere and from there another stretch with no records until Rye Harbour Local Nature Reserve.

At one of the new 2002 localities the plant is colonising rocks recently imported to protect the harbour wall at Prinsted, Thorney Island. It is also found at Chichester Harbour north of Wickor Point, north of Great Deep and at Rye Harbour opposite the road at the Wader Pool hide.

Slender Hare's-ear

The Slender Hare's-ear is native around the Mediterranean and across Europe to Scandinavia, the Caspian Sea and Iran. It flourishes in a Mediterranean climate.

Small Teasel

Dipsacus pilosus

Teasel family
Dipsacaceae

Habitat: Damp places in open woods, by streams and in hedgerows, mostly on chalk
Height: 30-120cm
Flowering: August
Status: Scarce in Sussex
'Look-alike' plants: Distinguished from other teasels by the small rounded flower heads and growth habit

Small Teasel is a biennial native plant that has a tall, angled and furrowed stem, with some weak prickles on the angles. The basal leaves are in a rosette, broadly oval, pointed, and narrowed into a long stalk; the stem leaves have a short stalk. The rounded flower heads are about 2cm across – when they are young they droop, but later straighten out on long prickly stems. The individual flowers are only 6 to 9mm wide and whitish with distinctive dark violet anthers. The scales on the flower heads are tipped with spines.

Small Teasel is scarce in East Sussex, with only two known sites at Seaford and Netherfield. In West Sussex there are 12 localities, and in many of these the populations have in recent years increased in size. This is especially so around Arundel, Little Bognor and West Grinstead.

The name 'Small' Teasel for this tall plant refers to the small rounded flower heads, that are much smaller than the common Wild Teasel *Dipsacus fullonum,* which has much larger blunt conical flower heads up to 8cm long, and spiny bracts between the florets. The Wild Teasel is common across Sussex on chalk and clay, often appearing unexpectedly and conspicuously in hedgerows and on waste ground. In early autumn the seeds attract goldfinches, making it a useful plant for the wild garden. The flower heads with straight spiny bracts were formerly used to raise the 'nap' on newly woven cloth, as was the cultivated variety, Fuller's Teasel *Dipsacus sativus*, in which those spines curve back and 'teased' the fabric even more effectively.

Small Teasel

Small Teasel grows in England and Wales as far north as south Lancashire and Yorkshire. In central Europe it grows from Spain east to the north Balkans and south Russia, and north to Denmark and Sweden. It is also found in West Africa and Japan.

Tree-mallow
Lavatera arborea

Mallow family
Malvaceae

Habitat: Cliffs and waste ground near the sea
Height: 60cm-3m
Flowering: July to September
Status: Extinct as a native plant in Sussex, but several introductions
'Look-alike' plants: Common Mallow and Marsh-mallow (see page 148)

Tree-mallow is a handsome branched shrubby biennal with stout stems that are woody at the base. The upper stems are softly hairy with star-shaped hairs which can be seen with a x10 hand-lens. The stalked leaves can be up to 20cm long and are roundish, heart-shaped and these too are softly velvety with starry hairs. The flowers are on a terminal spike (similar to smaller flowered garden hollyhock) and 3 to 4cm across with broadly blunt overlapping petals, pale rose-purple marked with deep purple veins. The flowers have a double calyx of fused sepals. The fruits are wrinkled yellowish nutlets ridged along the back. Tree-mallow does occur as a native plant in Britain, but now only westwards from Dorset.

In Sussex it was first recorded in 1805 and throughout the 1800s, it was thought to be native or at least very well established in the county. Currently we have more than 20 recent sites from East and West Sussex, but all of these are now considered to be escapes from cultivation. Many of these sites are those where the soil is nutrient-enriched, such as those at seabird roosts, and some where seaside householders have dumped their garden rubbish.

Around Britain's coast the Tree-mallow is decreasing, however, it can also be found on Mediterranean and Atlantic coasts of Europe from Spain to Greece, and also in north Africa and the Canary Islands.

Tree-mallow

Wall Germander

Teucrium chamaedrys

Dead-nettle family
Lamiaceae

Habitat: Chalk grassland
Height: 4-14cm
Flowering: July to September
Status: Red Data Book
(Endangered) and Scarce in Sussex
'Look-alike' plants: Wild Thyme,
with which it is intermingled in the
Cuckmere cliff-top turf

There are fewer than ten sites of this delicate plant in Britain. Only one of these sites is in Sussex, at Cuckmere Haven.

On the cliff-top chalk grassland at Cuckmere the Wall Germander plants are very small and extremely difficult to find when not in flower. Not only are they small and inconspicuous, but they are also intermingled with the superficially similar Wild Thyme. The leaf shape is very characteristic though, and the flowers (when present) are strikingly different.

The plants are perennial, dwarf, evergreen shrubs (often only 4 to 6cm tall). The leaves are oval and about 1cm long with deeply toothed margins with rounded teeth, shiny dark green above and rather leathery, hairy and paler on the under surface. The leaf-like bracts below the flowers are similar to the leaves but smaller and the stalkless flowers are pinky-purple, with a 5mm tube. There are four sharp lobes to the upper lip, and a broad oval lower lip that is narrowed at the base. Like all germanders the lower lip has the shape of an 'afternoon tea' apron, being broadly oval with a wavy edge. The flowers are pollinated by bees.

Wall Germander

An old site for Wall Germander was on the walls of Camber Castle where it was first recorded in 1690. A manuscript in the British Library *Adversaria Petiveriana*, is the account of a botanical tour from London to Dover via Tunbridge Wells and Hastings written by James Petiver describing the journey with his friend James Sherard. They were both apothecary botanists (early pharmacists) and on one particular occasion forded the River Rother from Winchelsea to Rye on horseback. After an oyster breakfast in Winchelsea, they explored Camber Castle while waiting for the tide to drop and found the Wall Germander growing plentifully on the Castle Wall *"looking towards Rye"*. When the Castle was excavated in the 1960s, 70s and 80s considerable conservation effort went into protecting the plants, and they survived the renovations until 1991 when they were inadvertently destroyed by herbicide spray.

Wall Germander is often grown on rockeries and walls in gardens, but this is the larger, less compact hybrid of *Teucrium chamaedrys* and *Teucrium lucidum*. This hybrid is sometimes found naturalised away from gardens.

The colony of true Wall Germander at Cuckmere Haven is said to appear to be exactly similar to colonies in French chalk grassland across the Channel – so just possibly it could be a relict from before the time when the Channel cut through.

Wall Germander also occurs in central and southern Europe and south west Asia.

Weasel's-snout (Lesser Snapdragon)
Misopates orontium (Antirrhinum orontium)

Figwort family
Scrophulariaceae

Habitat: Cultivated ground on sand or gravel
Height: 20-35cm
Flowering: July to October
Status: Scarce in Sussex
'Look-alike' plants: Betony – but the leaves and shape of flower are different

This erect annual is sometimes downy with glandular hairs above. The 3 to 5cm leaves are linear, without teeth at the edges. The pinkish-purple flowers are almost stalkless and grow in the axils of the upper leaves. They are strongly two-lipped, with the upper divided into two lobes, and the lower three-lobed and closing the 'mouth' of the flower. The tube below is broad and swollen at the base. The lower lip is blunt and rounded, and not entirely convincing as being like the snout of a weasel! – it is more like a baby rabbit, or another name for this flower is Calf's-snout.

Weasel's-snout is an attractive plant which was formerly frequent in West Sussex as a weed of cultivation on sandy soils, but is now only occasional. It has always been rare in East Sussex, but now it is decreasing nationally. Recent Sussex records have been mostly from allotments, where it has been abundant near Chichester – also from field edges.

Weasel's-snout grows in the Mediterranean region, east to the Himalayas and south to the Canaries.

White Horehound (Marvel)
Marrubium vulgare

Dead Nettle family
Lamiaceae

Habitat: Short grassland, open ground and waste places
Height: To 60cm
Flowering: June to November
Status: Nationally Scarce and Scarce in Sussex
'Look-alike' plants: Downy Woundwort
(but this does not grow in Sussex)

The stems and leaves of White Horehound are downy with soft white hairs. As a native perennial wild flower it grows in sparse chalky grassland near the sea. This aromatic plant has long been used in medicine and Geoffery Grigson (1958) suggests that "*it must have been cultivated in this country for more than 1000 years*".

White Horehound has branched stems and roundish deeply toothed leaves, that are 1.5 to 4cm long. The two-lipped whitish flowers are in many-flowered whorls up the stems, where they are mostly pollinated by bees. The survival of White Horehound depends on the grassland habitat being kept open by grazing or disturbance so that the seeds will germinate freely in bare broken ground.

This aromatic plant was known to the ancient Greeks and recommended by Dioscorides (512 B.C.) for coughs – and also as an antidote to poison. The Anglo Saxons used it as a medicine for lungs, and Tudor herbalists praised it for coughs. *Syrupus marrubii* was included in the *British Pharmaceutical Codex* (1949); cough mixtures and throat medicines containing Extract of Horehound can still be bought today from herbalists. It is also one of the ingredients in some widely available throat lozenges. A local Sussex name for the White Horehound was 'Marvel', possibly because of its 'marvellous' healing properties.

Horehound has a long history of cultivation as a valuable herb, as well as

White Horehound (Marvel)

an ornamental plant. Many of the current records in Britain are likely to be of naturalised escapes from old cultivation. In Sussex White Horehound has never been common, with roughly ten sites scattered across the counties. The earliest Sussex record dates from 1789 from *"about Brighthelmstone"* (now Brighton). Through the last century White Horehound was known in Arundel Park in several areas and described as *"plentiful in valleys north of Swanbourne Lake and towards Whiteways"*. In the 1960s and 70s there was a colony on the slope above the lake close to the Swanbourne gates. Then for a dozen or so years those plants were not seen, and they were missed, particularly as there is a theory that the name 'Arundel' is derived from the old Sussex pronouciation of *Horehound*. However by 2000 three 'new' colonies had been found in the park further north. An old colony at Halnaker Hill was also refound with an additional new locality nearby in West Sussex, and in East Sussex there are records from Rye Harbour and on the cliffs above Beachy Head lighthouse – it is a plant for which it is certainly worth keeping a keen lookout.

White Horehound is found throughout Europe except for the far north, and also in north Africa, the Middle East and further east throughout Asia.

White Mullein
Verbascum lychnitis

Figwort family
Scrophulariaceae

Habitat: Open bare ground on chalk
Height: To 1.5m
Flowering: July and August
Status: Nationally Scarce and Scarce in Sussex
'Look-alike' plants: Distinguished in Sussex by the white flowers from other similar mulleins that have yellow flowers

This tall handsome plant, eye catching when grouped in numbers, has an angled stem with short, star-shaped powdery white hairs. The narrowly oval leaves, 15 to 20cm long, are dark green and almost hairless above, but are dense with white starry hairs on the under surface (important characters separating White Mullein from other mullein species). On the flower-spike, groups of two to seven white flowers, which are 15 to 20mm across, grow from flower stalks over 6mm long with whitish bracts below. The stamens have roundish orange anthers and anther-stalks (filaments) with shaggy white hairs. The flowers are pollinated by insects and there is copious seed production.

The appearance of White Mullein is often associated with sudden clearances of vegetation and tree felling, as after the Great Storm in 1987, and in the clearance for building the by-pass at Arundel. In the first years after clearance many new colonies of White Mullein sprang up on the bare chalk in the newly opened spaces – from seed long buried in the soil. The seeds are long lived and remain viable for many years. As other vegetation increasingly colonises in the following years, the White Mullein plants are crowded out and colonies can disappear for some time.

White Mullein

In Britain White Mullein is mainly a plant of south east England, with some records from the south west (including a few colonies with untypical yellow flowers). Records further north are mostly introduced plants as White Mullein is grown as a garden plant. In the wild it is a plant of disturbed ground and waste places on chalk. It is not unusual to find some of the yellow-flowered mullein species growing in a colony of White Mullein as hybrids between the species do occur.

We have no recent records for East Sussex but records from nine localities in West Sussex – but although these are all post-1986 some may have now become overgrown. Most recently White Mullein was seen on the Bury Hill escarpment, but it is well worth keeping a lookout in other chalk areas, as new plants can appear any year especially following tree clearance.

Beyond Britain, White Mullein grows in north-central Europe from France to Denmark, and in Morocco.

White Ramping-fumitory
Fumaria capreolata ssp. *capreolata*

Fumitory family
Fumariaceae

Habitat: Hedgebanks, waste ground and field edges
Height: Climbing 30cm-1m
Flowering: May to September
Status: No longer classed as Nationally Scarce.
'Look-alike' plants: Other larger fumitories

White Ramping-fumitory is a robust plant with thin-textured leaves cut into many oblong segments, smooth and often blue-green in colour. The conspicuous flower-heads have up to 20 densely crowded flowers at the top of the flower stems, white but partly suffused with pink or a deep purple-red. The individual flowers are 1cm or slightly longer, each with the upper petal spurred at the base. The characteristic fruiting capsules are about 2mm across, with rounded blunt tops and stout rigidly curved stalks. The flowers of the fumitories are very intricate, and for a positive identification a detailed *Flora* with measurements and keys for the flowers and capsules is required.

In Sussex we have over ten recent, scattered sites and in most of these the plants have not persisted for more than two or three years. We do, however, have two interesting historic records: at Bexhill it was first discovered by Markwick in 1832, and can be found there still, on pavement edges and by garden fences; and in Henfield where the Sussex botanist William Borrer cultivated many interesting plants in his garden in the 1800s. His house and garden have been built over, but still some of the plants from his catalogued garden can be found in nearby hedgerows, by footpaths, allotments and along field edges.

White Ramping-fumitory

Fumitory is a Medieval name which is derived from the Latin *fumus terrae* or 'smoke of the earth'. Fumitory plants were probably given this name because their greyish finely cut and divided leaves are somewhat smoke-like.

In Britain this plant is sometimes found in arable land and gardens, however it is declining in most of its inland sites. It is also occasionally found on coastal sites. White Ramping-fumitory grows in central and western Europe, where it can be abundant, and also in the Mediterranean region.

Wild Liquorice
Astragalus glycyphyllos

Pea family
Fabaceae

Habitat: Grassy places and scrub on chalk
Height: 50cm-1m
Flowering: July and August
Status: Scarce in Sussex
'Look-alike' plants: The size of the plant and the colour of the flowers does distinguish this from other pea family plants in Sussex

Wild Liquorice is a hairless, shrubby, perennial with a stout spreading rootstock. The 10 to 20cm leaves are divided into four or five pairs of opposite, and one terminal, oblong leaflets. The rounded oval cluster of cream-coloured or greenish flowers are on a stalk much shorter than the leaves. The flowers are followed by curved, pointed and spreading pods 25 to 35mm long.

The name 'Wild' Liquorice has resulted from this plant's resemblance to the cultivated Liquorice from southern Europe. Cultivated Liquorice has been grown in England since the time of Elizabeth I – mainly in Yorkshire, but also in Godalming and in gardens nearer to London for the markets there. It is a larger plant than Wild Liquorice, with larger roots sold as a sweetener and for medicinal use.

Wild Liquorice records are very scattered through Britain to southern Scotland, and through central Europe east to the Caucasus and Asia Minor.

Wild Madder
Rubia peregrina

Bedstraw family
Rubiaceae

Habitat: In hedges and thickets on stony ground
Height: 30-100cm
Flowering: June to August
Status: Rare in Sussex
'Look-alike' plants: Shrubby growth and size distinguishes from other British bedstraws

Wild Madder grows as perennial evergreen stems or a bush with a long, creeping rootstock and scrambling-ascending stems. These stems are rounded at the base, but above they are sharply four-angled; the angles being rough with downturned prickles. The rigid oval leaves, 1.5 to 5cm long, are leathery and shiny on the upper surface, with the edges and the midrib on the underside rough with curved prickles. These leaves appear in whorls, with usually four to six leaves in a whorl. There are clusters of 5mm flowers at the ends of the stems which each have five pale yellowish-green petals with a pointed tip. The tiny roundish black fruits are 4-6mm across.

Like the cultivated Madder plant grown for its red dye, Wild Madder was used as a dye plant. The dye from the root of the Wild Madder gave not red, but a rosy pink dye which was formerly popular for dying wool and fabrics.

In Sussex Wild Madder has always been rare. However, it is no longer considered Nationally Scarce, even though it grows only in south and south west England, and in the coastal counties of Wales northwards to Caernarvon. Wild Madder also grows in south west Europe and north Africa.

193

autumn

Autumn Lady's-tresses
Spiranthes spiralis

Orchid family
Orchidaceae

Habitat: Short permanent grassland and downland
Height: 5-15cm
Flowering: Mid-August to late September
Status: Not Scarce
'Look-alike' plants: Other species of lady's-tresses, but these are unknown in Sussex

This enchanting little orchid grows upright with several overlapping pale green scale-like leaves on the stem. A basal rosette of four or five oval, elliptic bluey-green leaves overwinters from early September to early in the following summer. This rosette then withers but the flower spike, in the autumn, appears from its centre. A new rosette forms alongside the spike, already in place for next year's flower. This unusual growing pattern means that the flowers and the leaves appear to be unconnected. The flower stems are densely covered with white hairs, giving the plant a soft furry look, and have up to 20 day-scented fragrant flowers in a single tight spiral around the stem. The tiny trumpet-shaped flowers are 6 to 7mm long. Unlike most orchids there is no spur.

There are records of Autumn Lady's-tresses from Elizabethan times, and it could be found in large numbers in a good year. In Sussex we have many scattered populations from downland slopes where the grass is short. There

autumn

Autumn Lady's-tresses

are also some lucky people who have Autumn Lady's-tresses on their lawns. These lawns are often derived from downland turf. The leaf rosettes are flattened very close to the ground and can be missed by the mower. The flower stems grow quickly so that that flowers seem to 'suddenly appear' on the lawn. In years when there is very little rain in August and the lawn mowers are left in the garden shed, small colonies of the orchid may suddenly appear and flower. A Slinfold lady who had Autumn Lady's-tresses on her lawn told me that she knew when she woke-up in the morning if her orchid flowers had opened from the fragrance floating in through the open window.

These pretty flowers can also be found on sports grounds and in some years there have been many plants in flower on Christ's Hospital School playing fields and on a disused grass tennis court in a garden near Horsham where Autumn Lady's-tresses flowered along the lines of the court. This is possible because the lines marking out the court provided sufficient lime to counteract the slightly acid soil of the court. A good place to see Autumn Lady's-tresses in large numbers is Bexhill Cemetery East Sussex, where in some years there are many thousands.

Autumn Lady's-tresses grows in England and Wales, north to Westmoreland and north eastern Yorkshire, and is reasonably common in the west and south of Ireland. In Europe it is found north to Denmark and central Russia; also in northern Africa and Asia Minor.

Cut-grass (Rice-grass)
Leersia oryzoides

Grass family
Poaceae

Habitat: At the edge of water along ditches in water meadows, by ponds
Height: 30-50cm
Flowering: (August) September to early October
Status: Red Data Book (Endangered), Schedule 8 and Scarce in Sussex
'Look-alike' plants: Reed Canary-grass when plants are non flowering

This native grass is now very rare in Britain with very few remaining sites, three of which are in West Sussex. Cut-grass grows in tufts at the water's edge on nutrient-rich mud, but in early summer months it can be difficult to distinguish from other grasses, particularly Reed Canary-grass with which it often grows. Both have flat, pointed leaves which are the same shade of yellow-green and superficially the grasses are very similar at that stage. The easiest way to identify Cut-grass is by 'feel' – the edges of its leaves have finely-spined margins, and the grass will live up to its name when fingers are run gently up the grass. The upper sheaths of Cut-grass also have short bristly reflexed hairs, but in spite of the rough leaves the grass is sweet tasting to cattle and may be grazed.

The grass is very dependent on the weather each year and flower spikes open only in years when a warm spring is followed by hot sunny weeks in late summer. In many years the flowering spike does not open at all, but remains furled in the rolled-up sheath giving the grass shoots a very characteristic outline of a bulge below the top leaf. This top leaf is set at what has been described as a 'jaunty' angle. The Cut-grass is then quite easily recognisable in

Cut-grass (Rice-grass)

late summer. Those flower spikes growing out of the sheath and opening in suitable years are wind pollinated; but those remaining furled are alternatively self-pollinated and ripe grains can be formed within the sheaths.

In West Sussex the largest colony of Cut-grass is at Amberley Wildbrooks, where it occurs along the edges of many ditches across the Brooks. The grass is very specific in its habitat requirements here, growing at the top edge of the bank above the water, but very seldom in the water or in the grassland away from the ditch. For more than 20 years at Amberley, a team of local botanists has monitored and counted the Cut-grass plants – it was found that the Cut-grass grows best on banks of managed clean water ditches that are trampled and grazed by cattle. Regular dredging of the ditches, the maintenance of good water quality free from pollution and grazing to keep the plant communities open are all necessary, so careful management of the site is essential for the survival of this very rare grass. This work is currently undertaken by the Royal Society for the Protection of Birds on behalf of the Sussex Wildlife Trust.

The smaller colony in West Sussex is at Shillinglee Lake where Cut-grass grows along a short length at one corner of the lake, and has survived the raising of the water level for the fishing interests. Older records in Britain were from marshy fields, but the Cut-grass has disappeared from this habitat through increased drainage.

There are still a number of smaller colonies in Somerset and in two other localities there have been attempts to transplant and re-establish some Cut-grass to sites under threat or from where the grass had become extinct – successfully at the Basingstoke Canal but without success in the New Forest. Cut-grass has been recorded from southern Finland to Spain, eastwards to temperate Asia and North America, but it has markedly decreased throughout the whole of Europe.

Notes on naming

The complexity of naming plants is largely due to the huge number of flowering plants in existence around the world, possibly over 300,000 species. In Sussex we have approximately 2,000 species of flowering plants and ferns. This number fluctuates as some sadly become extinct, while others are spread – often by human activities – and become established.

Most plants in Sussex have an English name, many of which have been in use for centuries and show the careful observation of our forebears who obviously knew the plants well when choosing the names. There is a standard list of English names prepared by the Botanical Society of the British Isles for use in legislation (for example in the Wildlife and Countryside Act 1981). These are the English names used in this book. At the same time we are anxious that local names for wild flowers should not be lost and forgotten – if any readers know of old Sussex names for the wild flowers, we would be pleased to hear of these.

Internationally, Latin names for plants are invaluable, and these formal scientific names in Latin are laid down by the international code of nomenclature. Botanists working on this classification are continually learning more about the plants, and from time to time some Latin names are submitted to be changed to fit the increasing knowledge gained about those plants.

Prior to the current system of scientific Latin names (developed in 1735) descriptive names in Latin were given to plants, each of these could be several sentences long and were very clumsy. The brilliant Swedish botanist, Carl Linnaeus, then devised a system of grouping basically similar plants into families, and in turn regrouping into a smaller unit with more closely similar characters, a *genus*. Within the genus a second and descriptive name is then added to the plants, giving to each plant an individual species name.

For example, Round-headed Rampion has the basic characters of

the Campanulas, so is in the **family Campanulaceae**. However it is separated from other groups (genera) in the *Campanulaceae* family by its congested flowerheads, the placing of the bracts, curved flowerbuds and linear stigmas, all characteristic of the Rampion **genus Phyteuma**.

Our Sussex Rampions are then separated from the 24 Rampion species that grow mostly in the Alps and mountain meadows of Europe. They are found occasionally growing on dry grassland or in woods and meadows as in the case of our Sussex Rampions. Our Round-headed Rampion is then distinguished by the globular flowerheads from which it gets its specific name '**orbiculare**' so **Phyteuma orbiculare** is the scientific name for this wild flower.

At times plants can vary quite considerably in appearance but in general the key characters remain consistently diagnostic. Only experience helps to decide when the variations are significant. Remember that the plants don't read the books!

About Sussex Wildlife Trust

The Sussex Wildlife Trust was formed in 1961 (then the Sussex Naturalists' Trust) by a small group of enthusiastic volunteers with a common aim to conserve the rich wildlife heritage of East and West Sussex, which even then was being threatened by changes in the social and agricultural structure. The Trust is now a professional body with full-time staff and over 15,000 members. Its aims are the same today as in 1961, but now the Trust has a much wider remit. Sussex Wildlife Trust is one of 47 Wildlife Trusts, working together for wildlife at regional, national and international level.

The Trust takes a broad approach to conserving wildlife. It manages over 30 nature reserves in East and West Sussex, covering over 1,350 hectares. These sites are often havens for rare or endangered species, many being Sites of Special Scientific Interest or with other statutory designations recognising their importance for wildlife. They are important for people too, providing opportunities to experience nature at first hand. Most Sussex Wildlife Trust nature reserves are open to the public.

Environmental education is a major part of the Trust's work. There are two education centres at Woods Mill and Seven Sisters Country Park. We also teach groups of children in their own school grounds, classrooms and in the field about wildlife, within the framework of the National Curriculum.

The Trust also runs special projects, such as the Sussex Otters and Rivers Project, which endeavours to improve habitats so that wildlife returns to them. The Trust also works within the Biodiversity Action Planning process.

If you would like more information on Sussex Wildlife Trust and how to join please visit www.sussexwt.org.uk or telephone 01273 492630.

About the Sussex Botanical Recording Society

The Sussex Botanical Recording Society is a group of botanists whose aim is to study and record the distribution of wild plants in East and West Sussex. The society is the successor to the Sussex Flora Society, which was responsible for producing the *Sussex Plant Atlas* in 1980. Our members, work resulting in the *Supplement to the Sussex Plant Atlas*, covering recent changes in the Sussex Flora, was published in January 1991.

Our members are involved in a range of projects, which currently include recording for the Botanical Society of the British Isles, performing surveys of nature reserves and other areas of conservation interest, as well as for interested farmers and landowners. As a result of these activities we have established contacts with the Sussex Wildlife Trust, East and West Sussex County Councils, the Forestry Commission, the National Trust and the Royal Society for the Protection of Birds. We maintain close links with the Botanical Society of the British Isles via the county recorders for East and West Sussex who are members of our committee.

Each year we hold up to 12 field meetings in the spring, summer and autumn and two indoor meetings (usually in November and March). Members also receive two newsletters each year. The autumn meeting always includes a short talk by one of the members: recent topics include "The Orchids of Sussex", "Amberley Wildbrooks" and "Arnold's Flora of Sussex". Field meetings are held in all parts of East and West Sussex to undertake surveys requested by landowners and conservation groups, and to survey areas of special botanical interest. Some meetings concentrate on particular plant groups and aim to improve members' knowledge, recent examples being meetings that focused on wild roses and ferns.

We can undertake botanical surveys either as individuals or as a larger group. Following a survey we provide lists of plants present in the area together with further information about those species which are of particular interest and, where appropriate, advice on their conservation. Although most of the work of the society is concerned with the flowering plants and ferns we have some members whose expertise extends to the 'lower plants' such as mosses and lichens.

If you would like further information about the Sussex Botanical Recording Society or would like to make use of our expertise please contact our secretary, Rita Hemsley, 32, Dumbrells Court, North End, Ditchling, Hassocks BN6 8TG.

About the Sussex Biodiversity Record Centre

The Sussex Biodiversity Record Centre is a partnership funded initiative hosted by the Sussex Wildlife Trust at Woods Mill. It aims to collect and collate information on the species and habitats of Sussex in order to respond to the numerous enquiries that it receives each year.

In order to carry out this work the Record Centre liaises with a wide range of biological recorders, including the Sussex Botanical Recording Society. Groups such as the Sussex Botanical Recording Society, and many individual recorders kindly provide their records to the Centre in the understanding that this data will help inform decision makers across East and West Sussex.

For further details about the work of the Sussex Biodiversity Record Centre please visit www.sxbrc.org.uk

About the Author

Mary Briggs M.B.E., F.R. Pharm. S. developed an interest in wild flowers as a child and has taken this interest from Sussex, to a national level and then all round the world.

She is President of the Sussex Botanical Recording Society and was for many years President of the Botanical Society of the British Isles. She is still an active botanist in Sussex between leading tours for botanists and wild flower enthusiasts in South Africa, the Alps and the Mediterranean. She has led tours in 23 different countries, which has further developed her fascination in plant distribution.

Mary, who was a founder member of the Sussex Wildlife Trust, and was also a Trustee for many years, has been the driving force behind key contemporary Sussex botanical literature including *The Sussex Plant Atlas* (1980) and *The Sussex Rare Plant Register* (2001).

She continues to travel extensively and her lifetime's experience and knowledge has inspired and encouraged many botanists, and wild flower enthusiasts from Sussex and beyond – over many years.

Book list

Here is a list of interesting and helpful books. Some of these publications may be 'out of print' but should be available secondhand, via the internet or in libraries.

Flower Identification

Field Flora of the British Isles
An abridged version of the *New Flora of the British Isles* (2nd edition 1997). No illustrations but with keys, measurements and standard English names. Also the most recent Latin names.
1999 Stace. Cambridge University Press ISBN 0521653150

How to Identify Wild Flowers
700 original illustrations, aimed to help the reader identify with confidence. Selected species only.
2000 Grey-Wilson & Alderson. Trafalgar Square ISBN 0002201070

Wild Flowers of Britain and Northern Europe
Concise guide to the trees, shrubs and flowering plants of Britain, Ireland and Europe from the Arctic to the Alps.
1996 Fitter, Fitter & Blamey. Collins ISBN 0002200627

The Concise British Flora in Colour
1486 species illustrated; brief descriptions with paintings. These paintings capture the 'jizz' of the plants; includes grasses, rushes, sedges and trees.
1982 Keble Martin & Joseph. Collins ISBN 0718121260

Wild Flowers of the British Isles
Ecologically orientated text with colour illustrations of all species. Grasses and sedges not included.
1983 Garrard & Streeter. Macmillan

The Wild Flower Key: British Isles and North-West Europe
Clear illustrations and helpful keys
1981 Rose. Warne ISBN 0723224196

Wild Flowers of Britain
Photographs used, and species usefully arranged by flowering time.
1983 Phillips et al. Pan ISBN 033025183x

Reference Books
Grasses
Comprehensive descriptions and detailed drawings of each species of grass
in Britain. An invaluable aid to identification of this large and difficult group.
1988 Hubbard. Penguin Books ISBN 0140132279

Wild Orchids of Sussex
All our Sussex orchids described in detail with biology, history and
distribution map – and stunning photos.
2001 Lang. Pomegranate Press ISBN 095334933

A Field Guide to the Trees of Britain and Northern Europe
Concise descriptions of our native and planted trees in Britain.
1978 Mitchell. Collins ISBN 0002192136

Mediterranean Wild Flowers
Descriptions and illustrations of Mediterranean plants including some that
can survive in the Sussex climate.
1993 Blamey & Grey-Wilson. HarperCollins ISBN 0002199017

Umbellifers of the British Isles
Diagnostic drawings and detailed descriptions, including chemistry and uses
of this widespread and difficult to identify group (Apiaceae).
1980 Tutin. BSBI Publications ISBN 090115802x

Philip's Street Atlas – West Sussex
Countryside features are marked.
2001 Ordnance Survey ISBN 054008029

Philip's Street Atlas – East Sussex
(As above) Ordnance Survey ISBN 0540079715

Further Reading

Flora of Sussex
A detailed Flora including illustrations and botanical and geological maps.
1937 Wolley-Dod. Saville. Hastings

Flora of Sussex: Second edition
A list of flowering plants and ferns found in the county of Sussex.
1907 Arnold. Simpkins, Marshall, Kent and co. London (1st ed 1887)

The Englishman's Flora
Fascinating accounts of the uses, history and poetry. Long lists of the old local
names for wild flowers in each county across England.
1955 Grigson. Phoenix House ISBN B0000CJA21

Flora Britannica
The history, folklore and uses of our British wild plants.
1996 Mabey. Sinclair Stevenson ISBN 1856193772

The Great Yew Forest
The natural history of Kingley Vale.
1978 Williamson. Macmillan ISBN 0333227395

Guide to Medicinal Plants
A guide to 400 plants as used by doctors and herbalists for centuries.
1990 Schauenberg & Paris. McGraw-Hill ISBN 0879834897

Furze
Traditional uses and history of Gorse in Ireland.
1960 Lucas. The Stationery Office for the National Museum of Ireland.

Lords and Ladies
A whole book on this one plant called: 'the outstanding eccentric of our wild flowers' – with fascinating chapters on its many local names and uses.
1960 Prime. Collins New Naturalist Series ISBN B0000CKMVN

Arum Italicum (Italian Lords and Ladies) in Sussex
A historical review of the current status
1998 Clough. BSBI News 79:55

Handbook of Medicinal Mints – Phytochemicals and Biological Activities
The mint family including an explanation of the effect of Catmint on cats.
2000 Stephen, Beckstrom-Sternberg & Duke ISBN 0849327245

Useful websites

Botanical Society of the British Isles
www.bsbi.org.uk

Natural History Museum
www.nhm.ac.uk/science/projects/fff/Search.htm

Sussex Wildlife Trust
www.sussexwt.org.uk

Sussex Biodiversity Record Centre
www.sxbrc.org.uk

Wild Flower Society
www.rbg-web2.rbge.org.uk/wfsoc

Royal Botanic Gardens Kew – Wakehurst Place
www.rbgkew.org.uk/visitor/visitwp.html

Plantlife
www.plantlife.org.uk

English Nature
www.english-nature.org.uk

Booth Museum of Natural History
www.booth.virtualmuseum.info

High Weald Area of Outstanding Natural Beauty
www.highweald.org

Chichester Harbour
www.conservancy.co.uk

Ashdown Forest
www.ashdownforest.org

Sussex Downs Conservation Board
www.vic.org.uk

Botanical books and hand-lens suppliers

Summerfield Books
The Arches, Main Street, Brough, Cumbria CA17 4AX
Tel 017683 41577 Fax 017683 41687
www.summerfieldbooks.com

East and West Sussex maps

More information and detailed maps for Sussex Wildlife Trust nature reserves are available at www.sussexwt.org.uk

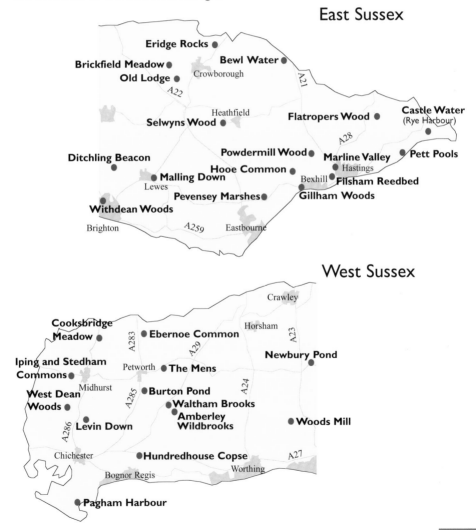

East Sussex

Eridge Rocks ●
Brickfield Meadow ●
Old Lodge ●
Bewl Water ●
Crowborough
A22
A21
Heathfield
Selwyns Wood ●
Flatropers Wood ●
Castle Water
(Rye Harbour)
A28
Ditchling Beacon
●
Powdermill Wood ●
Marline Valley ●
Pett Pools
Hoee Common ●
Hastings
Malling Down ●
Lewes
Bexhill ● Filsham Reedbed
Pevensey Marshes ●
Gillham Woods
Withdean Woods
Brighton
A259
Eastbourne

West Sussex

Crawley
Cooksbridge
Meadow ●
A283
Ebernoe Common ●
Horsham
A23
A29
Newbury Pond
●
Iping and Stedham
Commons ●
Petworth ● The Mens
A24
West Dean
Woods ●
Midhurst
A285
Burton Pond ●
Waltham Brooks ●
Amberley
Wildbrooks
A286
Levin Down ●
Woods Mill ●
Chichester
Hundredhouse Copse ●
A27
Worthing
Bognor Regis
Pagham Harbour ●

Glossary (alphabetical)

Botanical terms

Achene: a small fruit (which develops in a flower) – not splitting open when ripe

Alternate: (of leaves) see diagram on page 214

Annual: a plant which grows within a year

Aril: (of yew) a fleshy covering enveloping the seed

Auricle: an 'ear-like' growth, often at the base of a leaf

Axil: the upper angle between a stem and a shoot or leaf

Basal: (of leaves) growing from the root or base of the stem

Biennial: taking two years from germination to the end of the plant (usually flowers in second year)

Bract: a modified leaf, usually just below a flower and/or a bud

Bracteole: a second, smaller bract

Bulbil: a small bulb growing from a leaf axil

Calyx: a collective term for the sepals forming the outer covering of a bud around the petals

Capsule: a dry seed container, splitting open when ripe to release the seeds

Chlorophyll: the green colouring in plants (sunlight + carbon dioxide + water = carbohydrates + energy)

Disc florets: tubular florets in the centre of a daisy shaped flower

Elliptic: not perfectly circular, slightly egg-shaped with equally narrowed or rounded ends

Evergreen: with leaves that remain green throughout the year

Filament: (anther stalk) see diagram on page 214

Floret: a small, single flower that is part of a flowering head made up of such florets

Foetid: unpleasant smelling

Keel: (of flowers) the boat shaped, fused lower petals of a flower in the Pea family

Lanceolate: (of leaves) lance-like, narrowly egg shaped, longer then broad

Linear: (of leaves) slender, elongated with parallel edges

Opposite: (of leaves) see diagram on page 214

Ovate: egg shaped

Parasitic: describing a plant without any chlorophyll that obtains all it's nutrients from a host plant

Perennial: a plant lasting for more than two years

Pinna: (of fern) the first division of a divided fern leaf

Pinnate: feather-like leaflets in two rows along the branch of a stem

Pruinose: frosted with white (as on the skin of a dark plum or grape)

Ray-florets: outer strap-shaped florets of a daisy-shaped flower

Rhizome: a specialist stem growing underground, producing roots and the above ground growing parts of the plant

Rew: a Sussex term for a thin strip of woodland dividing fields

Spadix: a fleshy spike often surrounded by a spathe, as in Arum Lilies

Spathe: a conspicuous leafy bract surrounding, often overtopping a spadix

Stamen: male part of a flower with anther and a filament producing pollen

Stigma: female part of flower that receives the pollen

Stolon: a prostrate or trailing stem taking root from which plantlets grow at its top or along the stem or leaf junctions

Style: the narrow part of the carpel between the ovary and stigma

Tap root: the first and main root. It anchors the plant after germination and delivers nutrients to the plant

Tendril: a slender modified stem, which can attach to a support by twining and spiralling

Tuber: a swollen underground stem or root used for storage

Umbel: a flat or rounded-topped inflorescence with groups of small flowers on the tips of rays (stems) which all arise from the same point at the top of the flowering stem.

Whorl: of leaves or flowers arranged in a circle around a stem

Other useful terms

Taxonomy: the science of classification. Botanical taxonomists decide where plants fit in the plant kingdom and give each plant its Latin name.
Sussex Scarce: less than four sites in either county (East and West Sussex now being distinct counties).
Nationally Scarce: found in more than 16 but less than 100 10km squares in Britain.
Red Data Book: this lists the rarest species in Britain giving the legal status of each. Those included are all threatened or near-threatened species of vascular plants in Britain. The current *Red Data Book* which we use is the *British Red Data Books, Vascular Plants 3rd Edition*. There are also data books for mosses, lichens and other groups of plants, as well as many for other groups of wildlife. Many other countries now also have produced *Red Data Books* for their endangered plants.
For further information go to:
www.jncc.gov.uk/communications/pubcat/rdb.htm

Parts of a flower

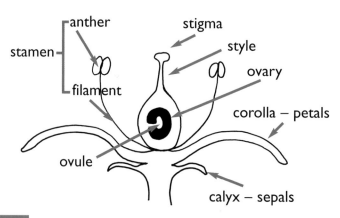

Alternate leaved

Opposite leaved